Somewhere In The West

Texas Women Who Left a Legacy

Poems and Legends by Linda Kirkpatrick

Edited by Janice Coggin

Cowboy Miner
PRODUCTIONS

Somewhere In The West Texas Women Who Left a Legacy
Poems and Legends by Linda Kirkpatrick
Copyright © 2002, 2003 Cowboy Miner Productions

Illustrations Copyright © 2002, 2003 Linda Kirkpatrick
Edited by Janice Coggin
Produced by
   Cowboy Miner Productions
   P.O. Box 9674
   Phoenix, AZ 85068
   Phone: (602) 569-6063
www.CowboyMiner.com

Publishers' Cataloging-in-Publication Data

Kirkpatrick, Linda 1958–
Somewhere in the West : Texas Women Who Left a Legacy
   Poems and Legends by Linda Kirkpatrick / Linda Kirkpatrick.
   Edited by Janice Coggin.
   p. cm.
   ISBN: 1-931725-01-2

1. Cowboy—Poetry. 2. Women of the West. 3. Ghost Stories.
4. Christmas Poems. 5. Texas History.
   Historical Photos. I. Title
   Library of Congress Catalog Card Number: 2001098766

Book Design & Typesetting: SageBrush Publications, Tempe, Arizona
Jacket Design: ATG Productions, Cory Olson, Phoenix, Arizona
Printing: Print Partner, Phoenix, Arizona
Printed and bound in the United States of America

Dedication

This book is dedicated to some very special cowboys that have been in my life.

My first cowboy poem was written in memory of Marc Grissom, a little cowboy who is now living with God. My dad, Alton Kirkpatrick, is next in line. He gave me the experience necessary to write cowboy poetry. I know that as a young child I was mostly in the way, but I was allowed to hang around the pens and tag along behind the cowboys on my paint horse as they rounded up the stock. My granddad, Burl Kirkpatrick, could be seen following the sheep or goats, leading his horse. We never could figure out why he did this, but I think that he was giving the horse a rest and just enjoying his contact with the earth.

My uncle, Lloyd Kirkpatrick, found humor in every wreck and storm that happened on the ranch. If things got boring, he would do something funny to make us all laugh. My uncle, Joe D Tomberlin was a great storyteller. He cowboyed in West Texas when the cowboys still had to pack a pistol. He taught me how to milk a cow by pumping the tail up and down and how to appreciate a good horse.

My son, Douglas Brice, loves his cowboy heritage and is ready to rope at the drop of a hat. My grandson, Wade Brice, is following in the boot steps of his ancestors.

My friend, Frank Roberts, has been a relentless mentor. He has kept me writing and almost always has a few better words. To Joe Wells, who we call the educated, broken-down old rancher and who is a very good friend. And to all of my other friends in the cowboying work force: without all of you I would not be reciting and writing today.

Linda Kirkpatrick
September 2001

Linda Kirkpatrick and Surprise

Let the Rest of the World Go By

"With someone like you, a pal good and true,
I'd like to leave it all behind and go and find,
Some place that's known to God alone,
Just a spot to call our own.

"We'll find perfect peace, where joys never cease,
Out there beneath a kindly sky.
We'll build a sweet little nest, somewhere in the West,
And let the rest of the world go by."

—*J. Keirn Brennan*
Copyright 1919

About the cover:
"The Cabin on the Frio"

The cabin depicted on the cover is a well-known landmark in the Frio Canyon of Texas. It has been the subject of many photos and has adorned the cover of several magazines. In the spring you can often find artists, with paint and palette, rendering it on canvas. My mother, Bette Kirkpatrick, also painted the cabin on a Christmas ball. The ball hung on the Texas state capitol Christmas tree in Austin, Texas.

David and Babe Elms built this small cabin around 1886. As time moved on, several other families in the canyon would also call it home. The cabin now stands abandoned on the banks of the Frio River. It is located on the H. W. Lewis Ranch. The ranch is private property, but visitors to the canyon can enjoy its beauty and serene setting from the highway.

Contents

Foreword

In 1997 Linda requested that we critique a poem she was writing about the McLaurin Indian massacre entitled, "Conflict in the Frio Canyon." As her story unfolded, we were caught up in the emotions of that tragic occurrence. It was a revealing experience to hear part of our local history, related in verse, in a way that made it compellingly personal as if we had witnessed it ourselves.

That same year saw the beginning of the Cowboy Sunset Serenade, an entertaining and educational program that strives to pass on our western heritage as well as Texas and local history through cowboy songs and poetry. Reluctantly, Linda became a part of the program, and in her own unique style began to emphasize the importance of the women of the West.

In the ensuing years she has researched many important stories about these often over-looked figures of our past. Her intriguing stories move the listener through a range of emotions, while instilling the desire to learn more about the characters she presents.

In *Somewhere in the West*, Linda presents her stories of these women, as well as numerous other poems she has written. She paints a larger picture with her follow-up stories including historical facts and background information gleaned from her research.

Through the Cowboy Sunset Serenade, Linda has shared her stories with thousands of intrigued listeners. Since 1997 this program has been presented several nights each week at Garner State Park from Memorial Day to Labor Day. This, in addition to special performances at many state parks across the state of Texas, as well as cowboy poetry gatherings at Alpine, Lubbock, and Ruidoso, NM, museums, schools, civic organizations, private functions, and last, but far from least, the state capitol in Austin, Texas has allowed her work to be heard by an extended group of listeners.

It is our sincere hope that *Somewhere in the West* will further expand Linda's audience. For it is the written and spoken word that will best perpetuate the mystique of our unique heritage.

Long Live the West!

Frank Roberts & Joe Wells
The Cowboy Sunset Serenade

Frank Roberts (above)
and Joe Wells

Thanks Ya'll!

Thanking everyone who had a hand in this book would fill an encyclopedia. Several people do deserve special thanks. I'll begin with Lurlene Boren who showed me how to enjoy writing and Velma Burditt who taught me the keyboard. I hope that both of you are in heaven looking down at what you have created in me. Thanks to Jack Rushing, my seventh grade teacher, for "learnin" me how to think and introducing me to Texas history. Thanks to Genevieve Trees, my fourth grade teacher, who let me read all the books in our classroom. It took the summer before I went into the fifth grade to get the job done, but I did it.

Thanks to Bill Bradley, Ron Williams, and Michael Davis for reading, adding your insight, computer knowledge and being my friends.

Thanks to Gloria Carrillo, J. R. Martinez, and Sarah Morales for attempting to teach me Spanish. Your language is so beautiful.

Thanks to Janice Coggin and her wonderful staff for believing in my story.

Thanks to all my friends too numerous to mention.

And last, but not least, thanks to all my family, past and present. Because of you I have acquired a wealth of needed material.

Introduction
The Beginning

This book is the result of many years of reading, researching, and dreaming. I read about some of the material in this book when I was only six years of age. The entire book has grown out of a love for history, cowboys, and women of the west. Besides these stories, I have also discovered another genre that is included in this book, cowboy poetry. Cowboy poetry is a story with a rhyme and a meter. The first forms of cowboy poetry were actually told around campfires in the late 1800s. The cowboys who sat around these campfires were usually following a herd of cattle to some far away location, months and miles from home. For entertainment these cowboys would tell stories over and over until one night, one old cowboy told his story with a rhyme and meter. This small change in story telling made the story easier to remember and more enjoyable when the story was repeated more than once.

Cowboy poetry almost became a thing of the past just like the trail drives but recently cowboys from all corners of the world are bringing this form of poetry back into the light. But the cowboys now have competition from the cowgirls. The women are putting pen and ink to paper and adding their insight to cowboy poetry.

Though I write about the cowboy, most of my writings focus on the women of the west, women often found in the background. The women that you will find in this book had to manage homes, children, the needs of their cowboy, then be able to saddle up and "take up the slack" to keep the farm or ranch going. This was their life and they did this in order to survive. The lives of these frontier women have been romanticized. I hope to enlighten readers that these women did not just sit on the porch shelling peas and watching the children.

My goal is to honor and recognize these women. Some will never find their place in a history book and others only have small paragraphs allotted to them. Some have worked ranches while others gave their time and lives to several occupations, their contributions going unnoticed. This book will introduce you to a few of these women. Women who came west and stayed, making the best of the situations at hand.

Some of these women are wives, mothers, others are cowgirls, outlaws and prostitutes. The stories of these women are outstanding. I hope these words truly honor them and in honoring these women, I hope to have an impact on you, the reader.

So many women were called to the West with just the same thoughts as those written in the song "Let the Rest of the World Go By." It seems like the West has always had a romantic mystery that called and beckoned. The women who met this call were strong beyond their means. They faced hardships and struggles head on and never looked back.

Texas Women Who Left a Legacy

This section of this book is dedicated to the women of the West. Dedicated to the women who have lived in our past and have places in our history. Dedicated to the ones who will forever live within our hearts. They are so courageous.

Tribute

From pages worn in books of old
Eager to have their story told.

The diaries of these women gone
But their lives and loves linger on.

Like blossoms that again will bloom
Their fragrance to fill a silent room.

These women will live and again emerge
As from dusty pages their stories surge.

Though the pages are yellowed, cracked and torn
The lives we will honor and never morn.

We will read and live their lives once more
As tributes to these women soar!

When I began researching and writing about the women of the old west I became so upset as I read the diaries of some of these women. I was upset because none of the women in my past ever wrote down one single word. Well, heaven help my descendents because they are going to drown in all of my stories! I do have oral stories about my great grandmothers but am so envious of the descendents of the women who kept diaries. It would have been so great to read the words of my great-great grandmother Margaret Elizabeth Woods Fleming. It is told that she could shoot a chicken hawk out of the sky with her husband's Texas Ranger rifle. And how she would lay awake at night when he was gone with the rifle in hand and a butcher knife under her pillow, because she could hear the Indians outside their home.

The women that I have chosen to write about in this section are remarkable women and I hope that you enjoy their stories.

The Plight of Mary Millsap

In the predawn hours, he kissed them goodbye,
First his children, then Mary his wife.
He told them he loved them, tipped her his hat,
The scene you could cut with a knife.

"The Gonzalez Rangers must go and fight!
We must help save the Alamo!
The Mexicans will charge it, they need us now
Please Darling, please let me go."

Mary backed away as he mounted his horse
The horse shivered and tensed with fear.
Mary rubbed her hand down the bays lathered neck
Then slowly she wiped a tear.

The last words he told her, should he never return,
"To the river you must go.
Take the children, my love, and hide by the banks
You'll be safe where the waters flow."

They left with a thunder of hoof beats
Her oldest child's hand she did take.
They turned and walked to their homestead,
She thought that her heart would break.

The ticking clocks chimed the hours.
The hours then turned into days.
She listened for the sound of his voice,
The Alamo was so far away.

Fearfully Mary waited,
Her mind could see the stress
As Houston organized reinforcements
What he would do, she could only guess.

Then one day she heard the excitement,
A woman and child from the Alamo
Had brought the news that was dreaded,
As a haunting breeze did blow.

"No one has lived. The Alamo is gone.
They are all dead." These words she said.
"Santa Anna has won, we are all doomed.
Santa Anna is one to dread."

Susannah's words cut the air.
Mary said, "Come children, please lead the way.
We must go to the river, we must go now."
Then they went that very day.

What would she do at the river?
How long would they have to stay?
They had so little food and no shelter,
She wished he were here today.

The chill of late evening cloaked them,
The whisper of spurs cut the air.
Fear clutched their hearts, who could it be?
"Who is it? Who goes there?"

Mary drew her children near her.
"Are you the one's left behind?
We are looking for Mary Millsap,
We are looking for Mary who's blind."

She walked from behind the post oak tree,
Her oldest child held her hand.
She cried for her loss and what she must do,
She cried for the fate of the land.

Houston's guards told her that she must come,
To leave would be her best fate.
She could follow the troops like all the rest,
It was known as the Runaway Scrape.

Just a small part of Texas history
From pages battered and torn
Is told in this story of Mary Millsap
And of how this legend was born.

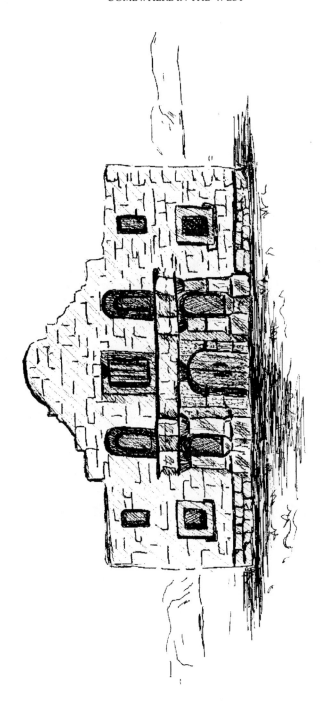

The Alamo

Widows of the Alamo

"The men of Texas deserved much credit, but more was due the women. Armed men facing a foe could not but be brave; but the women, with their little children around them, without means of defense or power to resist, faced danger and death with unflinching courage."

Thomas Rusk

"The younger and stouter women would take the feeble ones on their backs and shoulders and wade through the water to dry land, set them down and then go back for another load, and continued until all were over. There is no one who can do justice to the women at that time. God bless the women of Texas!"

S. F. Sparks

The women who came to Texas were strong beyond means. They faced every hardship and danger that one can imagine and still they survived. The following story is the tale of two of these women. The first is Susannah Dickinson who, along with her baby daughter Angelina, were the only Anglos to survive the Alamo. The second is Mary Millsap, the wife of Isaac Millsap who died March 6, 1836 at the Alamo. I felt compelled to add Mary's story as it was so intriguing in it's own right but also because my daughter-in-law and grandson are of the Millsap family.

The tolling bells of San Fernando alerted young Susannah Dickinson that danger was near. She grabbed her young daughter Angelina and ran to the plaza where she was met by her husband, Almeron Dickinson, who immediately loaded her and the baby on to the back of his horse and galloped for the protective gates of the Alamo.

Susannah Wilkerson of Hardeman County, Tennessee married Almeron Dickinson at the age of fifteen. Family stories tell how Susannah and Almeron were sweethearts,

but a spat caused Almeron to court another girl, a friend of
Susannah's. When the date for the wedding of Almeron
and Susannah's friend was announced, it was Susannah
who was asked to be a bridesmaid. In her heart, Susannah's
still pined for Almeron. She and Almeron realized that
they still really loved each other and the night before
the wedding, they saddled their horses and left a very
bewildered bride standing at the alter wondering what had
happened to her groom and bride's maid. Susannah and
Almeron then joined a group of colonists and found
themselves bound for Texas.

Almeron was a blacksmith by trade. When he and
Susannah settled in Gonzalez, Texas, his trade was much
in demand. Susannah was very aware of the hostilities
between the Texans and the Mexicans. She would wait and
worry each time Almeron was gone.

The families who arrived in Texas as part of Austin's
"Original Three Hundred" found various ways to deal with
the hardships of this new land. They even received
assistance from the Mexican *Comandante* at Bexar. The
settlers of the town of Gonzalez were exposed to Indian
attacks. To help stave off these attacks, the Mexicans gave
the settlers an old brass cannon to help in their defense of
the settlement. The gun was almost worthless but it was
presumed the loud noise might help scare away the Indians.

Most of the Mexican forces found in Texas at this time
were made up of *presidarios*. *Presidarios* were often the worst
convicts of Mexico. This posed a problem and was probably
the reason for the start of the war. The settlers had
problems with these convicts, and they did retaliate. The
incident at the town of Anahuac is just one example of
retaliation that may have sparked the flame.

The Mexican forces controlled the garrison at Anahuac.
These forces were made up mostly of the dreaded
presidarios. Four *presidarios* entered the home of one of the
settlers, where they discovered that the wife was home

alone. They then decided to take advantage of this helpless, or so they thought, woman. The woman shocked the men as a fight ensued. She fought, screamed and kicked with the fury of a mad woman. Nearby, hunters heard the commotion and rushed to her aid. The door was locked from the inside but this did not deter the hunters. They took a nearby post and battered down the door. Three of the *presidarios* escaped. The fourth, declared as the leader, barely escaped being hanged from the nearest tree. Since the captured *presidario* was a soldier of Mexico, the settlers decided that hanging would be too big of an insult to the flag of Mexico, but a warning to the rest of the garrison must be given.

The lone *presidario* was coated in tar from head to toe. The woman that he had helped abuse, took the feathers from her bed and covered the man with them. The *presidario* was then paraded through town and then returned to the fort with a message of warning. The Texans' message gave warning that if anything else like this happened there would not be a *presidario* left alive.

This incident resulted in the arrest of several soon-to-be heros including one named Bill Travis. This incident sparked a flame that would continue to burn throughout the land. The settlers met and words of revolution began to spread. The Anglo prisoners were soon released but in the minds of the settlers, the revolt was smoking on the horizon.

A few years after this incident at Anahuac, Capitan Castenado was sent to retrieve the old brass cannon from the settlers of Gonzales, by force if necessary. Captain Albert Martin sent messengers to the settlers in the surroundings areas to come to his aid. The war was on!

The young Lt. Almeron Dickinson was in charge of this brass cannon. The settlers taunted the Mexicans with the cannon and were determined that the Mexicans would not get back their cherished piece of artillery. On October 2, 1835, the settlers scattered the Mexicans with slugs and scrap iron that they had loaded in the cannon.

At this point the men of Gonzalez knew that the feared Mexican forces would be on the move. With this thought the people of Gonzalez began doing what they could to support the upcoming revolution. Settlers were to donate all their iron. The women brought in their flatirons, pots and pans. One woman even gave the spindle from her spinning wheel.

In the midst of preparing to march to San Antonio, the people of Gonzalez decided that they needed a flag. A committee was appointed and a flag design was adopted. Again the women of the town rallied. The committee was given material in the form of the ladies cherished silk dresses. These dresses were in all shades and textures. One woman donated her only set of green window curtains.

The flag was to have a white field without a border and in the center a picture of the treasured cannon. Over the cannon a single five-pointed lone star was sewn and under the cannon the words, "Come and Take It"!

Susannah Dickinson and Mary Millsap may have been among some of the women who added their materials and time in the construction of the "Come and Take It" flag.

On the morning of October 13, 1835, the volunteers headed toward Bexar with Almeron as artillery commander. This body of volunteers consisted of five to six hundred men.

During the siege of Bexar, the Volunteers found many women and children hiding in the homes that they had raided. These Mexican women, like the Anglo women, showed strength unheard of today. They offered the Volunteers food and cared for the wounded from both sides. One little girl even offered her pet kid goat as food for the hungry soldiers.

The siege of Bexar ended on December 10, 1835. The volunteers returned to their homes weary and tired but jubilant after their victory. They would soon be called to return to Bexar. Almeron Dickinson was one of the volunteers that came home to Gonzalez. On his return trip to Bexar, he took Susannah and his baby daughter Angelina. They set up housekeeping at the Ramon Musquiz home on the Main Plaza. It was here that they lived, until the day the bells tolled.

Almeron took Susannah and the baby to the Alamo. A small group of men soon joined them and it was here within the walls of the Alamo that they would make their stand. It should be mentioned that the volunteer army consisted of less than two hundred men while the Mexican forces numbered in the thousands.

The situation inside the compound walls of the Alamo was disheartening. Every day they continually hoped that help would come. The messages they sent requesting help fell on deaf ears and the help never arrived.

Travis' poignant letter requesting help from the people of Texas was a stirring one.

> *Commandancy of the Alamo*
> *Bejar, Feby. 24th, 1836*
>
> *To the people of Texas & all Americans in the world*
>
> *Fellow citizens & compatriots*
>
> *I am besieged, by a thousand or more of the Mexicans under Santa Anna—I have sustained a continual Bombardment & cannonade for 24 hours & have not lost a man—The enemy has demanded a surrender at discretion, otherwise, the garrison are to be put to the sword, if the fort is taken—I have answered the demand with a cannon shot, & our flag still waves proudly from the walls—I shall never surrender or retreat. Then I call on you in the name of Liberty, of patriotism & everything dear to the American Character, to come to our aid, with all dispatch—The enemy is receiving reinforcements daily & will no doubt increase to three or four thousand in four or five days. If this call is neglected, I am determined to sustain myself as long as possible & die like a soldier who never forgets what is due to his own honor & that of his country—VICTORY OR DEATH.*
>
> *William Barret Travis,*
> *Lt. Col. Comdt.*

*P.S. The Lord is on our side—When the enemy
appeared in sight we had not three bushels of corn—We
have since found in deserted houses 80 or 90 bushels and
got into the walls 20 or 30 head of Beeves.*

Travis

The men of the Gonzalez Rangers answered Travis's
appeal. On March 1, 1836, thirty-two volunteers, including
Isaac Millsap, entered the gates of the Alamo in support of
Texas independence.

James Butler Bonham, a messenger, galloped through
the gates and into the confines of the Alamo. He carried
with him the fateful news that Fannin and his troops would
never arrive. There would be no more reinforcements.

On March 3, 1836, Isaac Millsap penned a letter to his
wife Mary. There has been some question as to whether this
letter is authentic because the handwriting appears to be
different than the hand writing found on voter records that
were allegedly signed by Isaac. However, it is possible that
Isaac could neither read nor write and quite conceivable
that he had other people write for him and sign his name,
thus the difference in the handwriting. The letter is as
follows:

"*My Dear, Dear Ones,*

*We are in the fortress of the Alamo a ruined church
that has most fell down. The Mexicans are here in large
numbers they have kept up a constant fire since we got
here. All our boys are well & Capt. Martin in good
spirits. Early this morning I watched the Mexicans drilling
just out of range they were marching up and down with
such order. They have bright red and blue uniforms and
many canons. Some here at this place believe that the
main army has not come up yet. I think they are all here
even Santanna. Col. Bowie is down sick and had to be to
bed I saw him yesterday & he is still ready to fight. He
didn't know me from last spring but did remember Wash.
He tells me that help will be here soon & it makes us feel*

*good. We have beer and corn to eat but no coffee, bag I
had fell off on the way here so it was spilt. I have not seen
Travis but 2 times since here he told us all this morning
that Fanning was going to be here early with many men
and there would be a good fight. He stays on the wall
some but mostly to his room I hope help comes soon cause
we cant' fight them all. Some says he is going to talk some
tonight & group us better for Defense. If we fail here get
to the river with the children all Texas will be before the
enemy we get so little news here we know nothing. There
is no discontent in our boys some are tired from loss of
sleep and rest. The Mexicans are shooting every few
minutes but most of the shots fall inside & no harm. I don't
know what else to say they are calling for all letters, kiss
the dear children for me be well & God protects us all.*

Isaac

*If any men come through there tell them to hurry with
powder for it is short I hope you get this & know—I love
you all."*

In the early morning hours of March 6, 1836, Susannah
and the rest of the inhabitants of the Alamo heard the
haunting notes of *Deguello*. The *Deguello*, the trumpet song,
stands for no quarter to be given. As the last note floated
over the early morning sky of Texas, Santa Anna charged
the walls.

Through the heavy artillery smoke, Almeron found
Susannah within the sacristy walls of the old church. "Good
God, Sue, the Mexicans are inside our walls! All is lost! If
they spare you, save my child!" Susannah never saw
Almeron alive again.

In silence, Susannah and the Mexican women huddled
with their children against the wall wondering what their
fate would be. A Mexican officer entered the open doorway.
He looked at Susannah and told her if she wanted to save
her life she must follow him.

26

As Susannah stepped out into the courtyard she viewed a site that history books can never describe. The air was still heavy with smoke. The mutilated bodies of the Texans and Mexicans were piled in heaps around the courtyard. Later they would be engulfed in funeral pyres, sending their heavenly smoke and history to the skies above.

Despite the gunshot wound in her leg, Susannah was to be Santa Anna's courier to Sam Houston. It was from her lips that Houston's forces would learn about the fall of the Alamo.

Ben, the free black servant of Col. Almonte, was to escort Susannah and Angelina to the town of Gonzalez. Joe, the servant to Col. Travis, joined them along the trail. Joe had been spared during the siege but in fear had run away toward Gonzalez. These four would bear the sad news to the town of Gonzalez. Three scouts from Sam Houston's army of Gonzalez, Henry Karnes, Deaf Smith and Robert Handy, found them and escorted them the rest of the way.

The women and children of Gonzales met them as they entered the town. They soon learned they were widows and orphans. Longing for the last words of their loved ones, these strong women listened to every word that Susannah had to say. Among the widows and orphans stood blind Mary Millsap and her seven children. Mary, with the assistance of her children, followed the words of her husband and went to the river. Susannah delivered to Sam Houston the letter from Santa Anna. The letter, written March 7, 1836, was addressed to the citizens and inhabitants of Texas. The next evening, as Houston's remaining army burned the town of Gonzalez, the women and children fled behind the soldiers to east Texas in what would later become known as the Runaway Scrape. In the haste and confusion this rag tag group of people was several miles along the way when it was discovered that blind Mary and her children were not with them. General Sam Houston, when informed of this news, sent a group of guards to find the Millsap family. They found Mary and her children hiding in the brush near the river.

Susannah remained in east Texas for awhile after the battle of San Jacinto. She was witness to the beginning of the new Republic of Texas. She was denied aid because those in charge felt that this new Republic of Texas did not have the means to pay what was due her and the other widows. Thus, like many other women left alone in this vast new Republic of Texas, Susannah would turn to various desperate means. She was married to John Williams for a short period of time. This marriage ended in divorce. It was possibly the first divorce granted in the Republic of Texas.

Susannah ran a questionable boarding house until December 1838 when she married Francis P. Herring of Georgia. Mr. Herring left Susannah a widow a short time later. In December of 1847 Susannah married Peter Bellows. This marriage also ended in failure. When Mr. Bellows petitioned for divorce Susannah again returned to her boarding house as a means of support. She had by this time moved to the Lockhart area and life was about to take a turn for the positive. It was here she met and married Joseph W. Hannig. This marriage was a prosperous and happy one. The family moved to Austin in the late 1800s where they developed several businesses. Life again was good and happy for Susannah. She died in Austin on October 7, 1883, at the age of 68.

Susannah's daughter, Angelina, had a less fortunate life. She also had witnessed one of the state's most historic battles. It is said she led the life of a courtesan but perhaps not by choice. Guy Morrison Bryan proposed to the legislature that she receive three hundred dollars a year as the daughter of Capt. and Mrs. Almeron Dickinson. James Wilson also spoke in her favor. Favor was never granted. Angelina died at the age of thirty-seven, leaving behind four children.

Mary Millsap's life took a different turn. Left with seven children to rear alone and being blind proved to be a great burden for this very strong lady. When she realized that the widows and orphans were not to receive support she sent a plea to the Republic of Texas.

"To the Honorable member of the Senate and House of Representatives of the Republic of Texas in Congress assembled. Your petitioner the under signed begs leave to represent that she is the widow of Isaac Millsaps who fell in the Alamo on the 6th of March 1836. While fighting under the command of the gallant Travis, that in March 1835 he had made application for lands in Austin's colony which will be seen by reference to the books of that colony now in the general land office that about that time he selected and settled upon a League of land on the head waters of Labaca where he with his family resided when he was called to the defense of the country and where we were when they heard of the retreat of Houston and the advance of the Mexican forces. My self-blind and seven small children were not allowed one hour to prepare and no means of transportation we left all behind were thrown upon the world helpless and destitute in this situation. I have been struggling for 2 years and not able to return to the place we left. The prayer of your petitioner is that you pay an act to secure to me and my children land selected by my husband as I am informed that a man by the name of Jujac Roberson is making surveys that will interfere with my rights.

Mary Millsap"

Mary was granted two hundred dollars annually for ten years with one hundred dollars paid in advance. This payment was made on November 21, 1838. Mary was unable to pay the taxes on the 4,605.5 acres and on March 3, 1840 the land was sold for one hundred and fifteen dollars to James A. Sylvester.

Even though these three women suffered greatly, the strength that they showed is the strength that helped form the state of Texas.

Cynthia Ann Parker

The story of Cynthia Ann Parker is one that has always saddened me. Her life was torn apart by both of her families. Her white family and her adopted Comanche family each thought they knew what was best. They actually thought they were doing the right thing but in the end they realized the wrong that had been done.

It is impossible for one to totally be able to separate the factual history from the romanticized stories concerning the life of Cynthia Ann Parker. However, most of the basic facts are available and are told in the following story.

John Parker and Sally White, grandparents of Cynthia Ann, were united in marriage in the 1770s in Culpeper County, Virginia. This union produced six sons. Strong in the Baptist belief, the family stayed together moving from place to place always looking for something better. The family did face many hardships and in 1832 they looked south to Texas hoping for a more promising future.

The Parker family joined a congregation of Baptists that had formed in Illinois. This group began their journey towards Texas with twenty-five wagons. They crossed the Trinity River into Texas, then traveled to the headwaters of the Navasota where the settlement of Fort Parker was founded. The stockade walls measured ten to fifteen feet in height with the logs pointed at the top to discourage scaling of the walls. The fort also had two observation posts and cabins located within the protection of the walls.

Because of the recent threats of Indian attacks and the unsettled times with the Mexican forces, the Parker settlers abandoned the fort and tried to seek refuge in nearby Louisiana. However, because of a recent flood they were forced to wait for the waters to recede. During their wait they heard the news that Santa Anna had been defeated at the battle of San Jacinto and they were told that it would now probably be safe to return to the fort. Their safety was only a dream and their negligence led to their demise.

"If it is ordained that we should die here, then the Lord have mercy on our souls."

Elder John Parker

On the morning of May 19, 1836, the sun rose and sent shadows of light through the tall timbers surrounding the complex they called Fort Parker.

As smoke from the cooking fires spiraled upwards, the men prepared for their daily chores in the fields located outside the safety of the fort. Since Indians had not been seen in the area for awhile, the settlers had become relaxed and left the fort gates open.

It was probably around mid-morning when someone inside the fort discovered several hundred Indians had gathered outside the stockade. Assuming an inevitable attack, several of the fort's inhabitants tried to escape. The Indians (Comanche, Kiowa and Caddos) realized nearly all the men were gone from the fort and those remaining would be practically defenseless. Meanwhile, in order to stall an inevitable attack and in hopes that the men in the fields may have received a warning and would soon be returning, Benjamin F. Parker bravely walked through the fort gates and proceeded toward the group of Indians. He probably realized in his heart that he was facing a group of very hostile Indians and that defense was futile.

Ben returned to the fort to relay the news that the Indians wanted a beef. For some unknown reason and against the wishes of Silas Parker, Ben returned to again try to pacify the group of hostiles. Benjamin Parker was engulfed by a horde of Indians.

The inhabitants of the fort witnessed the brutal killing of Ben. In shock they watched as the attackers took advantage of the open gates. In a matter of moments the fort was besieged by a horde of Indians. As the Indians entered the stockade, the women and children ran in fear. The screams and cries echoing against the walls of the fort projected a living nightmare.

When the fort fell to a deadly silence, five settlers lay dead, five were captured and the remaining twenty-one fled in horror. The five that were captured were Cynthia Ann Parker, nine years old; John Parker (Cynthia Ann's brother), age six; Elizabeth Kellogg, a young woman; Rachel Plummer (expecting a child), in her teens, and James Plummer (Rachel's son) age two.

General Sam Houston later ransomed Elizabeth Kellogg for one hundred fifty dollars. Rachel Plummer suffered both mentally and physically at the hands of her captors. First she was separated from her baby son, James, and then six months later she gave birth to her second child. The baby was soon taken from her and killed. Rachel was ransomed about two years later by William Donoho. She was returned to her father's home where she died a short time later never to know that her first born, James, would be returned seven years later in 1842. The fate of John Parker is somewhat conflicting. One story states he lived with the tribe and married a Mexican girl and settled in Mexico. Another story states he was ransomed along with James Plummer. Assuming John was ransomed, this would leave only Cynthia Ann in captivity.

The word captivity now needs to be looked upon in various ways. Through the eyes of Cynthia Ann's family and the white society of Texas, Cynthia Ann was a captive of the feared Quahada Comanche. After her capture Cynthia Ann was adopted into a Comanche family. She soon assimilated into the tribe where she accepted her new home and way of life. Who can say or judge the life that she now led was not what was best for her?

Nothing was known of this young, now Comanche girl, until 1840 when she was spotted with a group of Comanche on the Canadian River. Col. Leonard Williams tried at that time to purchase her but the Comanche refused.

The year of 1840 proved a decisive year for Cynthia Ann and her anglo family. It would confirm that a peaceful return of Cynthia Ann would never happen. The Parker family would continue to grieve for her while she was only concerned with the care of her husband, Peta Nacona, and her children.

For a short time it seemed that the Comanche and the whites might make peace. On January 9, 1840, three Comanche chiefs met with Texas Ranger Henry Karnes hoping for a treaty. Karnes assured them there would be no peace treaty unless all the white captives were safely returned. The chiefs were to return in twenty days with all their white captives. They would then sign a treaty of peace with the Rangers.

It should be noted here that the new policy ordered the death of all Indians, the promises of the Rangers would not be kept. Texas was desperately trying to rid the territory of all Indians with little thought given to the long-term result. The Texans had three companies of infantry on hand when the Comanche made their promised return.

Now the Comanche on the other hand probably had their own plan even if it wasn't a successful one for they arrived at San Antonio on March 19, 1840, with only one captive, Matilda Lockhart. Matilda Lockhart had been captured on December 9, 1838. Unlike Cynthia Ann who had been captured two years earlier, Matilda's life with the Comanche was not pleasant. She had been given to the Indian women and was treated as a slave. When she was returned as part of the agreement between the Comanche and the Rangers it was noted that most of her body was scared from burns.

So on March 19, 1840 when the soldiers realized Matilda was the only captive that was being returned they immediately surrounded the building where the meeting between the chiefs and the Rangers was being held. The soldiers entered the building, creating a nightmarish situation.

Upon being informed that the chiefs would be held as prisoners until the other captives were returned, chaos erupted. Thirty-five Comanche were killed and twenty-seven were taken prisoner.

Revenge lay in the hands of the Comanche. During the first weeks in August the Comanche prepared their revenge. They proceeded from their haven on the Texas plains toward the coast, eliminating every white settler they found. On August 8, 1840, they struck the small port town of Linnville. They left the town at nightfall, leaving behind many dead and a town destroyed. With them they took several captives, horses, mules and the wares of Linnville.

The taking of Linnville by the Comanche stirred the hearts and souls of the people of Texas. Troops gathered to overtake the Indians who were hindered with the plunder and the many horses and mules. Troops under the leadership of Matthew Caldwell planned to intercept the Comanche at Plum Creek. Upon reaching Plum Creek, Caldwell's men were reinforced by several other companies of Rangers and militia.

On the way to Plum Creek the Comanche killed and plundered any settlement they came across. No white settlers were safe at this time from the revenge seeking Comanche.

Early in the morning of August 12, 1840, the Comanche moved west from Plum Creek, unaware of the impending attack. The Rangers attacked and when the fight was over between sixty and eighty Indians lay dead. Three of the four captives taken at Linnville were recovered that day on Plum Creek. The battle of Plum Creek took its toll on the Comanche tribe; never again did they fight as a large group nor did they try to overtake a town. They chose to fight in small groups and attack only the unprotected homesteads.

Several years later Cynthia Ann was seen with the Comanche on the Washita River in Oklahoma. Many unsuccessful attempts were made to ransom Cynthia Ann.

Could it be possible that she stayed with the Comanche by her own choice?

Later, Agent Robert S. Neighbors unsuccessfully tried to persuade the reluctant Cynthia Ann to return, but his inducement failed and he made no further attempts.

Victor Rose supposedly saw her in 1851 and tried to talk her into coming with him, but because of her children and husband, she would not leave. Could it be this Cynthia Ann did not see herself as white anymore and she totally accepted the Comanche as her family? Obviously the white society never took this into consideration.

Cynthia Ann was the only wife of Chief Peta Nocona. To this union three children were born Quanah, Pecos, and Topsannah. The Houston Telegraph and Texas Register reported in 1847 that "Miss Parker...has married an Indian Chief and is so wedded to the Indian mode of life, that she is unwilling to return to her white kindred." Still her family never gave up.

The band of Peta Nacona continued to raid and wreak havoc in Texas. He became such a feared nemesis that the citizens of Texas asked Governor Sam Houston to help them. It is at this time that Capt. Sullivan Ross enters the picture. Much to the despair of Capt. Ross, Peta Nacona stayed ahead of the wave spawned by the chaos, continuing his raiding and plundering of the settlements. His Comanches raided the Sherman homesteads. Mrs. Sherman was the only one killed during this raid. It is presumed this might have been a revenge killing since the lives of Mr. Sherman and two children were spared.

Captain Ross and Charles Goodnight were hot on the trail of this Comanche raiding party. Along the way towards the Pease River they found a Bible that had once belonged to Mrs. Sherman. This find convinced them they were on the right trail.

Capt. Ross was desperate. He said the first man to kill and scalp a Comanche would receive a Colt revolver. The raid at the Pease River was tragic and Capt. Ross took great pride in reporting the onslaught. It was during this battle that Lt. Tom Kelliher chased a lone Comanche rider. As he was steadying his aim, the rider turned. To his surprise the rider was a female with a baby. It was later discovered this female had eyes of blue. This female, though very distraught, was treated with kindness through the eyes of the Rangers but through her eyes she was being ripped from her home and away from her husband and children. Also through the eyes of many Texans, the battle of the Pease River was a victory, but many stories fail to mention that many of the lives taken that day were those of women and children.

The captured white female was taken to Camp Cooper. When finally persuaded to talk, her first concern was for her two sons; she was soon reassured that no young boys had been found amid the dead. Many people were under the impression that this white female was Cynthia Ann Parker. If this indeed was she, this would make the second time in her life that she would be taken from her family. One cannot even begin to feel or understand her feelings at this time.

Col. Isaac Parker, uncle of Cynthia Ann, was summoned. The young woman was interviewed with no success. Finally Parker said to the other men with him that if this was his niece then her name is Cynthia Ann and at that moment the young woman rose and said, "Me, Cincee Ann."

Cynthia Ann, who was captured at nine, was recaptured at thirty-four. Once a prisoner of the Comanche, she was now a prisoner of her own white society.

Life for Cynthia Ann with her white family was unhappy to say the least. She was thrown into the public eye and everyone wanted to know about her life with, in their opinion, the heathen Comanche. Cynthia did not understand all of this and wanted to return to her Comanche family. Her white family could not understand and continued to "protect her from the savage life of the Comanche."

Isaac Parker took his niece and her baby daughter to his home in Birdville. It was here the family took her Indian clothing and replaced them with "white women's clothes." Cynthia Ann in some ways tried to conform, but in her heart she would always be Comanche.

Cynthia Ann and her daughter Topsannah, moved to the home of her younger brother, Silas, and then later she lived with her sister Orleana. Cynthia Ann would never adjust to the ways of her white family.

On December 15, 1863, Cynthia Ann was devastated again by the death of her five-year-old daughter. From this point on it is believed that Cynthia Ann slowly grieved herself to death. In a small cabin, during the fall of 1870, Cynthia Ann drew her last breath. Her life had been one of struggle and conflict. She had continually been pulled between two opposing cultures, neither concerned with her wishes, Cynthia Ann became a captive of both societies. Her soul was now free of the bonds of the two societies, but her spirit continues to haunt the hearts of those who wronged her.

Later, Cynthia Ann's son, Quanah Parker moved her remains to Post Oak Mission Cemetery. On December 4, 1910, another funeral service was held for Cynthia Ann. It was a combination of Comanche and English.

Cynthia Ann would have been proud of the achievements of her son Quanah. He is remembered as a fierce and brave Comanche who tried to preserve the culture of the Comanche Nation. He was a strong force of resistance in giving up the ways of the people. In the end a choice had to be made. He had to either lay down the arms of his people or possibly face the extermination of his proud tribe. He never stopped being a leader. He worked hard to gain a better life for the Comanche in the world of the white man.

It is remarkable that sixteen years before he gave his blessing on the town named after him, he was leading the

attack on Adobe Walls. Adobe Walls was a small isolated
settlement on the Texas plains, mainly just a stop along the
way for the new settlers. Even though the Comanche
plotted and planned their revenge on the settlement of
Adobe Walls, they were no match for the buffalo hunters
within the confines of the walls. The Comanche realized
that the guns of the white man were no match for their
bows and arrows.

The speech that he gave at Quanah, Texas was quoted
by the *Quanah Tribune-Chief* as follows:

*It is well, you have done a good thing in honor of a
man who has tried to do right both to the people of his
tribe and to his pale-faced friends. May the God of the
white man bless the town of Quanah. May the sun shine
and the rain fall upon the fields and the granaries be filled.
May the lightning and the tempest shun the homes of her
people, and may they increase and dwell forever. God
bless Quanah. I have spoken.*

Quanah was laid to rest beside his mother. On August
9, 1957 their remains were moved to the military cemetery
at Ft. Sill, Oklahoma. In 1965 Topsannah's remains joined
her mother and brother at Ft. Sill.

Quanah's red granite headstone is inscribed as follows:

Resting Here Until Day Breaks

And Shadows Fall and Darkness

Disappears is

Quanah Parker

Last Chief of the Comanches

Born – 1852

Died February 23, 1911

Cathay Williams

In a tiny shotgun cabin,
    Martha's baby girl was born.
A baby, born to slavery
    who no one could forewarn.
But Cathay Williams was determined
    and never was deterred,
Beginning her life as a house girl,
    being seen but never heard.

Then the Civil War broke out
    and the Union soldiers came
And taking Cathay with them
    her life would never be the same.
Cathay learned the ways of military life,
    became an accomplished cook.
She was sent to General Sheridan,
    a job she proudly undertook.

Then the Civil War ended
    and Cathay was finally free
And in seeking out her freedom,
    she found her place in history.
Her own way she wanted to make
    and a burden to no one be
So as a Buffalo Soldier
    she joined up in the 38th U. S. Infantry.

Cathay Williams became William Cathay
    and no one was to know
The secret of her identity
    as a soldier she did grow.
The troops moved west to Ft. Cummings,
    to keep the Apache at bay.
There were 101 enlisted men,
    among them William Cathay.

After two years as a Buffalo Soldier
    in the 38th Company A,
William went to see the doctor
    and her secret came out that day.
Discharged as a Buffalo Soldier
    Cathay did her very best,
As she continued to make her way
    in this land we call the West.

Because of her illegal enlistment,
    her pension passed her by
But she picked herself up
    and moved on never questioning why.
Life ended for Cathay Williams
    at the age of eighty-two.
She lived a long independent life
    a life that was tried but true.

So a salute to Cathay Williams
    the hero of this rhyme
A special woman of the west
    and a legend in her time.

This poem was another 8 *Second* winner on Omar West's Bar D web site. It was read by Omar West at Politicalfest in Philadelphia, Pennsylvania, during the Republican Convention in July of 2000.

Frank, Joe and I, *The Cowboy Sunset Serenade*, were thrilled beyond words when we were invited to help celebrate the founding of the Buffalo Soldier divisions. Of course at the time of their founding these units were not known as Buffalo Soldiers, this name came at a later time. This celebration took place on the steps of the state capitol in Austin, Texas. I was very honored to present this poem and to immortalize the life of Cathay Williams.

The end of the Civil War brought an end to slavery setting the black people free. These former slaves were free. But unable to adjust to this freedom they just wandered aimlessly. They were free but unable to find work. They were without an education so had little opportunity to succeed in life. The government did, however, help some of these free blacks by creating all black infantry and cavalry units, an extension of former regiments in which some of the black men had served. These units were under the direction of white officers. Through these units of cavalry and infantry, the life of the free black man found purpose.

It was the Indians who gave these black soldiers the name of Buffalo Soldier. The Indians compared the hair, beard and faces to the head of the animal they so respected, the buffalo.

Another group of blacks served their time as guides and scouts. This group became known as the Black Seminole Scouts. These men were part black and part Seminole Indian from the swamps of Florida. The slaves that escaped the plantations of the Deep South fled to the Seminole Indian tribes in Florida. They were not only given refuge but were allowed to make the tribe their home.

When I first heard the remarkable story of Cathay Williams in 1998, I realized that I would have to tell her story. Cathay Williams was born into slavery in 1842 in Independence, Missouri. At the onset of the Civil War, Union Soldiers took Cathay from the plantation where she had served as a house servant. Since the troops were in much need of a cook, Cathay was forced into a job about which she knew little. Cathay was moved from battle to battle during the war. Her final job of the Civil War was that of cook and laundress for General Phil Sheridan. Her close exposure to military life during the war gave her an insight that would later be advantageous to her.

At the end of the Civil War, Cathay found herself without a job. It is said she joined the newly formed black infantry with her cousin and a friend because she wanted to make her own living and not be dependent on relatives or friends. These units were for men and it was absolutely forbidden to allow the enlistment or the commission of a woman.

Since there was no medical examination, Cathay simply reversed her name to William Cathay, donned the attire of a man and joined up on November 15, 1866. It is said that Cathay was about 6 feet tall and with a large frame which proved to be a great asset to her disguise. Cathay served for two years before she was taken ill and had to report to the infirmary. Upon discovery that she was female she was immediately discharged.

Because of her illegal enlistment her pension was denied. Throughout the rest of her life, Cathay Williams ran a successful boarding house. I am sure she had no idea that people would be writing about her remarkable life. What a wonderful story it is for all of us storytellers.

Cathay Williams died in 1924 in Raton, New Mexico.

Mary Ann's Legacy

I rode to the edge of the caprock
And gazed at the canyon below.
I thought of a time and a lady,
And of her life of so long ago.

I watched the remains of her legacy
Thundering within the canyon walls,
While the red tailed hawk soared peacefully
Beckoning with its lonely call.

The preservation of the buffalo
Was the center of her dreams,
And because of this honored lady
The hunters were not supreme.

She had returned in desperation
To a Texas she'd once known.
Vowing to never leave the canyon
And to forever call this land home.

She saw to the needs of her husband
And to the cowhands on the old JA.
She was wife, mother, sister, doctor
And preacher when they'd lost their way.

Life in the canyon was lonely
Her chickens her closest friends
And her love for the land and the buffalo
Stayed with her until life's end.

Mary Ann Goodnight grieved and watched
As progress raised its vicious head
And as the way was cleared for progress
They shot the buffalo dead.

In the day she heard the rifles ringing
And at night the orphan calves bawl,
As these sounds echoed the canyon
With their haunting lonely call.

Her heart pained for the orphan babies
And her feelings she did convey,
So Charlie went out and roped two for her
The ancestors of these today.

The Bison herd was swallowed up
As if it had never been,
While the canyon walls loomed in silence
Mary Ann's buffalo lived within.

Millions once roamed the canyons
But now there are only a few.
But thanks to Mary Ann Goodnight
Hers are here for me and you.

I first heard the story of Mary Ann Goodnight from
Vicki Sybert, Wildlife Interpretive Specialist whose project
is the Texas State Bison herd located at Caprock Canyon
State Park. Vickie and I share a great love of history and
the little known facts that make for great stories. Vickie
told me that Mary Ann, or Mollie as she was more
commonly known, wrote in her diary of how she could hear
the ringing of the rifles during the day and the crying at
night of the buffalo calves whose mothers had been shot by
the hunters. I have heard the mournful bawl of mama cows
and calves at the time of separation and it is a sad one

indeed. One would have to have witnessed this sound to understand the full impact of these lines from Molly's diary.

Mary Ann Dyer married Charles Goodnight on July 26, 1870 in Hickman, Kentucky. They set up ranching near Pueblo, Colorado. The Panic of 1873 and the drought brought the Goodnights back to Texas. It was in the Palo Duro Canyon of Texas that the Goodnights entered into a partnership with John George and Cornelia Adair to form the JA Ranch.

However, the buffalo that inhabited the canyon became fierce competitors with the cattle that the JA Ranch was producing. In order to eliminate the competition between the buffalo and cattle, Charlie organized buffalo hunts. These hunts would play a great part in the near extinction of the Southern Plains Buffalo.

Molly's life in the canyon was lonely but she always claimed to be happy. From her husband, to the cowhands, to the chickens and the buffalo calves, Molly generously gave of herself.

Mary Ann's legacy is located at Caprock Canyons State Park, 100 miles southeast of Amarillo, Texas. Known as the official Texas State Bison Herd, these animals had ranged freely in the Palo Duro Canyon system until 1997. The current owners of the JA Ranch donated them to the state of Texas. Through DNA testing, genetics indicate that this herd is of pure bison strain. These bison are the last of the Great Southern Herd and descendents of the two roped by Charles Goodnight and given to Mary Ann to raise. So even though Charlie Goodnight is credited for saving the buffalo, it might be quite possible that Mary Ann had a hand in his decision.

Mary Ann's headstone reads:

Mary Ann Dyer Goodnight
One who spent her whole life in the service of others.

Mary Ann Goodnight

Courtesy of Panhandle Plains Museum

Chief Costelitos, Teresita, and unidentified woman in front of jacale (house). Fort Clark, Texas

From the photo collection of the Daughters
of the Republic of Texas Library

Teresita

There was an uneasy tremor in the ground
She knew something was not right.
Then she heard the pounding of the horses' hooves
And slowly she stood in fright.

The troops topped the ridge in the early morn
They arrived in a cloud of dust.
She turned and looked for her father
The chief, a man she could trust.

Her eyes sparkled like black diamonds.
Her hair was like a raven's wing.
And as she stood amid the chaos,
She could hear the Shaman sing.

Their homes were torched and set ablaze,
Through the clouds of smoke she could hear
The sounds of the cries of the wounded
And again she gazed in fear.

Costelietos was roped and drug by a horse.
She ran to assist the old man.
"Where is the respect?" she wanted to know,
"He is leader of the Lipan."

They seemed not to care and they fired more shots,
But soon, not another sound.
With a silence so deadly and a calm so serene
The tribe was soon gathered around.

Those that could walk were made to march.
The others would die alone.
They crossed the river then another moon more,
'Twas the last time she would see her home.

Teresita and her father marched like the rest,
At Ft. Clark they were entombed.
They would live the life of captives,
While life as a Lipan was doomed.

She would later become the bride of a scout.
She would ride with him each day.
For freedom she did this, relinquished her dream
Oh what a price to pay.

No longer to run as free as the breeze,
No longer her soul to soar,
No longer to live as a dove on the wing,
No longer a life as before.

To her new life she adjusted.
Her new freedom she did behold.
She loved her family and worked as a scout,
But still longed for her life of old.

It is amazing the life of Teresita and the last Indian conflict in the Frio Canyon would be the result of incidents that occurred because of Grant's Peace Policy. President Ulysses S. Grant on January 25, 1869, met with a delegation of Quakers. These Quakers believed the Indian policy should be founded on peace and Christianity rather than by force. The Friends, as they were known, urged President Grant to appoint men of religious conviction to the agency posts. The result of this meeting led to what would become known as Grant's Peace Policy.

A leading authority pointed out that Grant's Peace Policy was in effect "a state of mind, a determination that since the old ways of dealing with the Indians had not worked, new ways, which emphasized kindness and justice, must be tried." The ways were tried and the ways failed. The Indians were moved to reservations but never accepted the way of life that the people of the East thought would be best for them. The Christian groups still believed the Indians could be elevated and fought to keep their foot in the door in civilizing the Indian.

The Quaker leader, Lawrie Tatum, was the man who took charge of the Fort Sill reservation in late 1869. It was here that the black Tenth Cavalry under the leadership of Benjamin H. Grierson worked with Lawrie Tatum for what they believed was the good of the Indians who inhabited Fort Sill.

The Kiowas at Fort Sill were under the leadership of three strong chiefs: Lone Wolf, Kicking Bird and Satanta. These Indians continued resisting the efforts of the white leaders of the fort and by continuing to raid and plunder in Texas. After their raiding they would return to the safety of the reservations. Tatum begged the Indians to stop and continued with his belief that he could make peace and change their ways. His ideas were to soon die on the plains of Texas.

In May of 1871, at Salt Creek Prairie, a large group of Indians led by Satanta attacked a supply train of ten wagons driven by twelve teamsters. Five of the men escaped, the rest were mutilated. The Indians had overlooked and bypassed a smaller train earlier that day. On that train rode the General in Chief of the U. S. Army, William Tecumseh Sherman, who had come to Texas to inspect the frontier facilities and to validate the stories of the Indian depredations in Texas. It was on this trip that he learned of the murders and tortures at Salt Creek and realized how close the incident had come to him.

The resulting effects of the Salt Creek Massacre would continue until April of 1881 when events from the capture of Teresita to the death of Kate McLaurin would come together.

Tatum would forget his beliefs and insist on the arrest of Satanta and his leaders. Sherman and Grierson met with Satanta and some of his chiefs on the front porch of Grierson's house. When the Indians realized they were to be arrested they went for their arms. Sherman, who had anticipated such a conflict, had prepared in advance and upon his signal the black soldiers appeared at the windows. This conflict resulted in Satanta, Satank and Big Tree being confined to the post jail. Later, on their way to Texas for trial, Satank attempted escape and was shot. A judge in Texas convicted Satanta and Big Tree sentencing them to hang by the neck until dead. Satanta and Big Tree awaited their sentence at the Texas prison in Huntsville.

The people of Texas were jubilant of this decision. The officials in Washington then had their say and the sentence was changed to life imprisonment and later these two were pardoned. As a result, Tatum resigned his post.

The results of the Peace Policy would have grave effects on western history until the late 1880s. Many Indian chiefs' lives were written in books and they became legends in their own right. Some of these would be Victorio, Sitting Bull, Geronimo and Quanah Parker.

After the attack of Salt Creek in May of 1871, two more conflicts with the Native Americans would reflect on the life of a young woman by the name of Teresita. These conflicts would be Mackenzie's raid at Remolino, Mexico, on May 18, 1873, and the last raid in the Frio Canyon on April 19, 1881. Another important event that would affect the life of Teresita was the entrance of the Black Seminole into Texas. The Black Seminole would serve as Indian Scouts and guides for the U. S. Army.

The Seminole Tribe of Florida is a mixture of various cultures and circumstances; a mixture of Creek, Hitchiti, Apalachee, Mikisuki, Yamassee, Yuchi, Tequesta, Apalachicole, Choctaw, and Oconee as well as slaves who had either escaped or were stolen from plantations of the South were adopted into the Seminole tribe. The tribe grew in strength and numbers. They were a well-organized culture who fought well with words and weapons. Andrew Jackson said, "I would rather fight five hundred white men than do battle with fifty Black Seminole."

The Seminole and Black Seminole were moved to the Indian Territory of Oklahoma in 1830. Many of the Black Seminole escaped to Mexico fearing the Anglo slave hunters. Under the guidance of Chief Wild Cat and John Horse, the Black Seminole felt safe living in Catholic Mexico where slavery was prohibited. Living in the Florida Wilderness had given them the skills to become some of the best frontiersman of the West.

However, the slave hunters continued to plague the Black Seminole in their habitat along the banks of the Rio Grande. One night in 1852 as John Horse attended a fandango in one of the border towns, a fight broke out and John Horse was shot and captured by a slave trader. He was carried across the river into Texas. Upon hearing of the capture, Chief Wild Cat paid five hundred dollars in ransom for the return of his friend. To avoid more captures by the slave hunters, the Seminole and the Black Seminole moved further into Mexico and settled in and around Naciemento.

At the conclusion of the Civil War and the abolishment of slavery, the Black Seminole began to cross the Rio Grande into Texas. The settlers and travelers in Texas were being plagued by the retaliation of the Comanche and Apache. The U. S. Army under the leadership of Major Zenas R. Bliss of the 25th U. S. Infantry recruited the skill of the Black Seminole. The Black Seminole knew the land, the language, and the ways of the Texas Indians. This would prove to be a great asset to the U. S. Army. Their survival and fighting skills would be compensated with pay and rations. The families of these men would also be allowed to accompany the new recruits from Nacimiento, Mexico, to the land across the Rio Grande.

On July 4, 1870, Major Bliss mustered the Black Seminole at Fort Duncan, Texas. Fort Clark and Fort Duncan would be the primary south Texas homes of these men and their families. The first men to enlist for a six-month term were John Kibbitt, Joe Dixie, Dindie Factor, Pompie Factor, Hardie Factor, Adams Fay, Bobby Kibbitt, John Thompson, John Ward and George Washington. These new recruits would receive thirteen dollars a month, a Spencer rifle, ammunition, and cavalry issued wool clothing, which they were allowed to combine with their own Indian clothing. They had to furnish their own horses or they could use horses that had been captured from the Indians.

It was in this vast Texas land just north of the Mexican border that the Black Seminole Indian Scouts found their home. Descendents of these early Scouts are still in the area today. A stroll through the Seminole Indian Cemetery near Brackettville, Texas shows the older grave stones indicating these people had indeed been born in Florida.

In 1873, Lt. John Lapham Bullis was attached to the 24th Infantry quartered at Ft. Clark at Brackettville, Texas. Under agreement with Mexico, this attachment was allowed to pursue the Lipan-Apache and Kickapoos into their mountain strongholds in Mexico.

Ft. Clark, originally known as Ft. Riley, was established in 1852. The name was changed from Ft. Riley to Ft. Clark in honor of Major John B. Clark, an officer who died during the Mexican War. Tents and *jacales* (the photo on page 48 of Chief Costelitos and Teresita shows them standing in front of an *jacale*) served as living quarters for the early inhabitants of Ft. Clark, Texas. The limestone wall that surrounded the fort still stands today. Provisions for the fort came from Corpus Christi, a 30-day journey. Later the trading post of Las Moras, founded by O. B. Brackett became the provisional headquarters for the fort. The post and surrounding village of Las Moras was later renamed, Brackettville.

From March of 1873 to June of 1881 the Black Seminole Scouts took part in twenty-six campaigns. Not one fatality or serious wound occurred during these fights. Willie Warrior, a descendent of a scout, recalls the story his uncle told of the time the Indians threw dead animals into the water holes to stop the scouts from tracking them across the desert land. His uncle and the rest of the troop had to cover their mouths with their bandannas to keep from swallowing the maggots as they drank the water. Willie remembered asking his uncle why he drank the dirty water. His uncle replied, "You don't know how thirsty a man can get. You don't know what you will do."

Even though the Black Seminole played an invaluable roll in the settling of the west, they faced discrimination, indifference and violence. There was much confusion as to whether they were free people or slaves. The land promised was never granted and rations were cut, forcing many of the scouts and their families to return to Mexico. The scouts who remained would serve into the 20th century.

Because of Grants Peace Policy strong retaliation against the Indians was looked down upon. However, General Philip Sheridan realized the strength of the Lipan Apache and Kickapoo in the South Texas area.

On April 11, 1873, General Belknap, the Secretary of War and General Philip Sheridan arrived at Fort Clark supposedly to inspect the troops. However, a secret meeting was held with Mackenzie who was told to control the situation and to do it in his own way.

Mackenzie realized he would have to cross into Mexico in order to put a stop to the Indian raids. Would he be supported in this maneuver? Sheridan again told Mackenzie to assume the risk and that he and Grant would assume the responsibility should any problems arise. Mackenzie knew he had to act soon.

John Lapham Bullis and thirty-four Black Seminole Scouts joined the six troops of the 4th Cavalry under Col. R. S. Mackenzie. No one knew what was going to happen but Colonel Mackenzie. The troops began to question where they were going and what they were going to do as they arrived at the banks of the Rio Grande. All four hundred soon realized they were going to enter Mexico.

Mackenzie fully believed he had received orders to invade Mexico but it appeared to all that he had made his own decision.

The troops rode hard to get to the heart of the camps before the Indians realized they were on their way. In order to move faster, Mackenzie ordered the packs cut loose. The troops kept pushing further into Mexico despite the heat, dust, mesquite and prickly pear. Then they came upon the sleeping village of Remolino.

This surprise attack at Remolino, Mexico, took place on May 18, 1873. Mackenzie ordered the villages burned. From his eyes the raid had been successful. Many of the Indians had been killed, some escaped and some were taken captive.

It was during this raid of the camp, that Renty Grayson, a member of the Black Seminole Scouts roped a Lipan-Apache chief named Costelietos. Costelietos and his daughter, Teracita, were taken captive. Teracita would later become the wife of Scout James Perryman and would accompany him on the many treks made by the troop. Teracita, herself, was a good tracker and assisted in tracking many bands of Indians.

One must remember by this time Satanta and Big Tree who had been captured and tried were now released. These two chiefs continued to keep matters stirred. As the buffalo, the main food source of the Indian, vanished, the Indian had little trust in the government. It was at this time that Quannah Parker, son of the white captive Cynthia Ann Parker and the Quahada Comanche Chief Nacona, led an attack on a group of buffalo hunters at Adobe Walls. The two hundred warriors led by Quannah were no match for the small group of well-armed buffalo hunters. The Red River War had now begun.

The Battle of Palo Duro Canyon was an important battle in the Red River War. On September 19, 1874, Comanche were discovered at the head of Pease River. About twenty-five Comanche attacked an advance group of scouts. It was during this attack that Seminole Scout Adam Paine would win his Medal of Honor for gallantry in action and rendering invaluable service to Colonel R. S. McKenzie. The troops continued to pursue these small groups of Indians.

The bravery of the Black Seminole Scouts is cited by the fact that three other scouts would receive the Congressional Medal of Honor. Isaac Payne, John Ward and Pompey Factor were under the leadership of Lt. Bullis and it was their loyalty and bravery that saved him from certain death. In April of 1875 Lt. Bullis and these three men almost met their match. Near the Pecos River, at Eagle's Nest Crossing, a trail of Indians and seventy-five stolen horses were found. They soon discovered approximately thirty Comanche and the herd of stolen horses were about to ford the Pecos. Even though Bullis and the scouts were outnumbered, they dismounted and set up their attack. Bullis and the Scouts were soon outflanked

and realized they had to make an escape. The four broke
and ran for their horses. The scouts mounted and began
their retreat but soon noticed that Bullis was having trouble
mounting his young horse who had become frightened in
the melee. The scouts wheeled their mounts around and
returned to rescue their lieutenant. John Ward rode hell
bent toward Bullis. Bullis grabbed Ward's arm and mounted
behind him. For their bravery, Sergeant John Ward,
Trumpeter Isaac Payne and Private Pompey Factor would
be awarded the Congressional Medal of Honor.

Bullis continued to lead the Black Seminole Scouts until
the Indians abandoned Texas. He supported his scouts and
they believed in him. It was Bullis who performed the
ceremony that married the captive woman Teresita to the
scout James Perryman.

As the year 1881 rolled around there would be many
changes in the lives of the scouts and the army of Ft. Clark.
For one, Bullis would rise to the rank of brigadier general
and the scouts would make their last expedition into
Mexico in pursuit of the Lipan Apache who had murdered
Kate McLaurin and Allen Lease. One of the scouts would
be Teresita.

Seminole Indian Cemetery Brackettville, Texas
Above: Graves of Adam Paine and Isaac Paine
Awarded Congressional Medal of Honor. Note the eagle design.
Below: Pompey Factor, Awarded Congressional
Medal of Honor

John Ward
Awarded Congressional Medal of Honor
Seminole Indian Cemetery
Brackettville, Texas

Conflict In the Frio Canyon

At night 'neath the stillness of the towering bluff
You can hear her saddened cry,
As a mist engulfs your body
In a shroud that will mystify.

As you walk through the quiet stillness
You can feel her presence there
And now I'll tell you her story
So listen if you dare.

Shhh! Listen, listen and you can hear.
"Mother, Mother," young Maude cried.
"Go Maude run," says her mother,
"Run south by the mountain side."

John had left them early that morning,
Kate, Maude, Alonzo and baby Frank,
And a hired hand, young Allen Lease,
All alone on the riverbank.

They had worked hard all that morning
Carrying water for washing their clothes,
While high atop the rocky cliff
Danger perched in a menacing pose.

When all their chores were finished
They took to the garden plot.
It was a lovely cool April day
And the sun was not quite hot.

The Indians watched them all morning
As they quietly stalked their prey,
Then they descended the mountain
At an hour past midday.

The Indians started to ransack the house,
They pillaged and plundered the place.
They had no mercy in their eyes-
Only murder, malice, disgrace.

Kate heard the noise from the garden below
And said, "Allen, go check and see,
It sounds like the hogs are in the house,
Go run them off now would you please?"

So Allen knowingly went to the house
But unknowingly went to his death,
He died from the shot of a warriors gun
And sighed in his dying breath.

"Go, children run, over the fence!"
Kate cried even though she'd been shot.
She tried to give Maude the baby
And cried as she weakened somewhat.

Four times more Kate would be shot
As she tried to scale the fence.
She fell to the ground, the babe in her arms
As his body her blood did drench.

Kate lay there dying, covered in blood,
Maude wanted to ease her pain
And what she did defied all fate
As she ran to the house with disdain.

She left her mother all covered in blood,
She ran as the blood did spread.
She ran to the house, where the Indians were,
To retrieve a pillow for her mother's head.

The Indians saluted her bravery.
They stood in awe of her diligent run,
They left but they would always remember
The girl and the deed she had done.

Maude tenderly placed the pillow
And comforted as best she could
While her mother whispered to her,
"Go Maude, run, take the trail through the woods."

Maude hated to leave her mother,
She feared what the Indians had done.
She cried as she stood and looked about
Then turned south and began to run.

She ran to the home of the Fishers',
They couldn't believe the story she told.
A posse gathered to find the Indians
Before the trail could grow dim and cold.

John McLaurin rode hard to get home,
He had a premonition that all was not well.
It was John Leakey who gave him the sorrowful news
And they rode to that massacred hell.

On their arrival they found the carnage
That was revealed from brave Maude's run.
The Indians were gone but left their deeds
To be viewed in the setting sun.

They found Kate's life flickering
A few sighs were all that was left
But she knew her children were safe now
And with pain she drew her last breath.

The Indians are gone now along with Kate's life
But this story is alive today.
So listen again, listen once more
And listen to what she must say.

Shhh! You can hear her now.
Hear the words from her dying breath,
"Go Maude, run!" she cries.
These many years since her death.

So as you listen to the night birds calling,
And as you listen to the cypress trees sigh,
As you listen you can hear her voice now,
As she says her last "Goodbye."

The H. W. Lewis Ranch, where I spent my childhood, is located in a very remote area of Texas. The ranch encompasses Owl Hollow, whose draws and springs feed the Frio River, and Bull Head which feeds the Nueces River. It is very rugged terrain, covered with rocks, cedars and oaks. At the springs one could usually find arrowheads left many years ago by Lipan Apache or Comanche Indians. It was very easy for me to let my mind wonder as to what might have happened in these sacred places or what famous chief might have walked these hills. At six years of age I had a very vivid imagination. Hardy Lewis, grandson of H. W. is a friend and still allows me to go back to my childhood home and again be able to step back in time.

Most of my entertainment centered around the radio shows of Gene Autry, Roy Rogers and Dale Evans, and the Lone Ranger. I also enjoyed stories that were either read or told to me. I remember the times when a cowboy, Buck Miller, from a neighboring ranch and his son, Buck Bowie, would ride over to visit. This was usually about once a month. We always looked forward to this visit. Buck soon discovered my love of history and stories of the west. On one of the visits he brought a book written by A. J. Sowell that would spark a real interest in me. The book was a collection of short stories written by Mr. Sowell, a former Texas Ranger. The short stories, are a very vivid collection of incidences in Texas history. Little did I know at the time that one of the stories would follow me my entire life. Mr. Sowell's account of the incident at the McLaurin homestead is a story that has been retold by many historians and story-tellers to this day.

My mother would read to me the story of the tragedy at the McLaurin homestead over and over. She would take me to the site of the conflict and there I would imagine all the tragic events that had been read to me from Mr. Sowell's book. It was a tragic and graphic story to say the least. It was a story I wanted to hear over and over again. It was a story that would be forever embedded in my mind. I eventually became a member of the local Girl Scout troop and was so excited when Miss Sallye Godbold came to our meeting and told her eye-witness account of the story. Miss Sallye, as everyone called her, was the town historian. Her retelling of the events of that day was so compelling. But what was so thrilling to me was the fact that she had been a small child that day in April of 1881. She had stood beside the wagon road when the bodies of Kate McLaurin and Allen Lease were brought to Leakey for burial. Miss Sallye described vividly the creak of the wagons and the somber look on everyone's face as the cortege arrived in town with their sad cargo. She was even able to point out to us the exact spot where she had stood that day. She painted a picture in my mind of the sad, silent faces of the people who met the wagon. She was able to make me feel as though I had been standing right there beside her on that day.

As I got older I began to wonder what triggered the events of that day in April of 1881 and also about the events that followed. The correct answers will be forever lost in history but some of these facts are being unearthed today.

The early ancestors of the Lipan-Apache may have started their trek to the southwest as early as the 1300s. During the 1500s they were in the Pecos Pueblo region of New Mexico. Because of their nomadic habits there is little archeological information recorded about them.

As the Spanish explorers came to this region in the 1600s, they began to enslave the Apache and the Apache retaliated. It was at this time that we begin to see a conflict that would continue until the late 1800s. Who would have known at that time that the manner in which these people were dealt would have such a negative effect on culture for many years to come?

These earlier Apache became scattered and some of the bands almost became extinct. The Lipan-Apache became a separate tribe known for their skill with horses. They called themselves "People of the Woods."

During the 1700s life as the Native Americans knew it was facing drastic changes. These changes were slowly being made and were totally destroying the Native American way of life. Their mere existence was being threatened and warfare was becoming a more predominant way of life. It was either perish or fight. They, who had once conquered the plains, would become remnants on reservations. They, who had gardened and hunted, would become poverty stricken. They, who were warriors, would now be the homeless of the Texas frontier.

Three forces were vying for this land that would eventually become the state of Texas. The three forces were the Indians, the Mexicans and the Anglo. All three had a strong desire and need for this land. The end results were devastating for all three. The Mexicans were defeated and returned to Mexico. The Indian would face near extermination. The Anglo would be supreme but would face great losses in the process.

Perhaps the raiding and plundering was their method of trying to keep their dreams alive.

The Lipan Apache segregated into small bands of about four hundred people. They avoided aggressive encounters but in order to survive, became skillful warriors. The Anglos, Spaniards, and Mexicans continued to press the Lipan Apache until 1680 when they found themselves on the Llano Estacado and the Edwards Plateau of Texas. The Llano Estacado and the Edwards Plateau are remote areas of Texas and the Lipan Apache were able to become somewhat hidden in this wilderness. Because of their defense of themselves and their land, the Lipan-Apache were labeled as renegades and savages. The settlers considered the Lipan-Apache predators and despised them. They did not realize that they, as settlers, were invading a land that had been the home of the Native American.

In 1716, priests arrived in the Nueces River Canyon region of Texas. Their goal was to bring Christianity to the Indians. During this mission period it is estimated that there were about three to five thousand Lipan-Apache in this hill country region.

As the buffalo were slowly becoming extinct, the Lipan began to raid the ranches of the settlers. The Indians treated the cattle as if they were the buffalo. These conflicts would grow until the life of the Lipan-Apache, like that of the buffalo, was no more.

Another threat began to pressure the Lipan-Apache. The threat, located south towards the Rio Grande and the missions of the Nueces River region, was the Comanche. As the Lipan were driven further into the desolate areas of Texas and Mexico, they began to seek refuge within the walls of the Spanish missions. While the Spanish priests thought that they were being successful in Christianizing the Lipan-Apache, the Lipan-Apache were using the walls of the mission as a safe haven from the settlers, the Mexicans and the Comanche. It was basically their last ditch effort to save what was theirs.

The two missions in the Nueces Canyon were Nuestra Senora de la Candelaria at Montell, Texas, and San Lorenzo de la Santa Cruz near the present town of Camp Wood, Texas. In 1765, the Lipan-Apache began to realize that the protection they thought the missions could provide would not protect any longer from their greatest fears. The Comanche and anglos were moving closer and closer. Soon the mission doors and the relationship with the missionaries would close for good.

Warfare became the last hope and now the way of life for the Lipan-Apache. From this time forward it was either war or perish.

When Texas became a state in 1846, the Indian tribes of Texas felt more pressure from the new inhabitants of their land. As a state, Texas did not feel responsibility for the Indians and felt that the Indians were trespassing on the land that was now their state. The Indians, on the other hand, still considered the land theirs.

In 1858, Texas Ranger John S. (Rip) Ford took command and wreaked havoc among the Indian tribes of Texas. The words exterminate, ethnic cleansing, and genocide are the only words that define the goals of the new inhabitants of Texas.

In the 1860s and 70s the Lipan-Apache were found in small groups within the state of Texas. Some lived in the Indian Territory, some with the Mescalero Apache, some served as scouts, and some looked for revenge.

The quote of Black Elk, after the battle of Wounded Knee, expresses the thoughts of many Native Americans who lived during this time.

"I did not know then how much was ended. Then I look back now from the high hill of my old age, I can still see the butchered women and children lying heaped and scattered all along the crooked gulch as plain as when I saw them with eyes still young. And I can see that something else died there in the bloody mud, and was buried in the blizzard. A people's dream died there. It was a beautiful dream…"

Perhaps these were the thoughts of the small band of Lipan Apache, in April of 1881 when they found themselves on a high bluff overlooking the Frio River and the McLaurin homestead. It has been said they were savage. It has been said they were murderers. Perhaps they were just in their own eyes trying to return to a way of life that had been taken away and the only way to retrieve that way of life was to remove the intruders. One will never know what thoughts this small band had on that day.

The history of the McLaurin family, like so many other southern families who left their homes in the deep South and sought a new life in Texas, stretches back to the moors of Scotland. One of the first McLaurin's to set foot on American soil was Duncan McLaurin. He arrived in America with his wife and eleven children in 1788. The McLaurin families became farmers but at the end of the

Civil War they salvaged what remained of their lives and moved west. The move to Texas was more than likely an experience to say the least. The many trails to Texas are lined with graves of families and friends, and upon reaching this new land, many found that they had to make do with the barest of necessities. Their arrival also introduced them to the Indian. The settlers felt that the land was theirs for the taking and the Indian felt that the land was theirs to defend.

The elder John McLaurin and his family made their way to the beautiful valley of the Frio Canyon in 1872. They built a native limestone home with 24-inch thick walls on Flat Creek. The house still stands to this day.

The younger John McLaurin and his wife, Catherine Ringer McLaurin (Kate), had the following children: Mary Sytarys, Maude Lee, John Alonzo, and William Franklin.

This younger John was not satisfied with the original location of the homestead south of Leakey so he decided to move his family north of the small settlement. The conflicts with the Indian were few now and John felt that the move north would now be safe. The place he found is about six miles north of Leakey, nestled between two towering bluffs with the cool, serene West Fork of the Frio River flowing nearby. The Frio River flows between the bluffs creating a beautiful but yet haunting site.

Allen Lease was an orphan living with a step-mom and a combined family. In that day and time, fourteen-year-old boys were expected to do a man's work. It was a very hard time for these families and in order to survive, children old enough to help were sometimes sent to live with other families who needed them. Thus when John McLaurin, his wife and children moved to their new homestead north of Leakey, Allen Lease was sent to live with them and help them establish the new homestead.

Perhaps what happened that day in April of 1881 was just a robbery turned bad. It has been said that evidence showed the Indians camped on the bluff for a couple of days. Perhaps they were waiting for an opportune time to rob the house. Perhaps they just wanted to see inside a white person's home. Then again maybe they wanted to take advantage of an unguarded situation and seek revenge.

John probably felt secure as he left his serene home for his overnight trip to the Cherry Valley settlement. The land between the house and the river was ideal for Kate's garden. The house was most likely a crude log cabin just big enough for the family. They probably had a few free ranging hogs, a milk cow, and chickens. There was an abundance of wild game and produce from the garden. The family's necessities were adequately met.

This small band of Lipan Apache probably watched from atop the high bluff as John McLaurin rode away on the morning of April 18, 1881. They may not have felt secure enough to get a closer look at the home until they were sure he was gone for the night.

As the Whip-Poor-Wills sang their lonely call on the night of the 18th and as the cypress trees sighed on the riverbank and as the Katy Dids sang their evening songs, Kate McLaurin put her children down for the night. Atop the bluff a small campfire flickered and the stars began to send frescos dancing across the bluff overlooking the home. Could this peaceful scene be a misleading charade of the danger to soon come?

April 19th, 1881, was wash day for the family. While Kate prepared breakfast, Allen milked the cow and fed the hogs. After these chores were done, Kate and Allen hauled water from the river. This water would then be heated in the wash pots for washing the clothes.

The Lipan Apache probably watched as Kate and Allen carried water from the river for the morning wash. They probably watched as the family went to the garden to work, and then assuming this was an opportune time, they moved slowly and cautiously down the rocky bluff to the small log cabin. As they entered the house, no one knows what their motives were; was it food, clothing or just curiosity that spurred them on? What would they have done if young Allen had not gone to the house to investigate the noise that they made? They may have shot out of fear when Allen approached the house and they may have then turned their guns towards Kate, the last remaining threat. No one will ever know the reasons for what happened that day.

By around nine the washing was finished and the clothes were scattered on the fence and bushes to dry. It was still unknown to Kate and Allen that all of their activities were being observed by a group of unknown and unwanted observers.

Sometime in the early afternoon, John Thompson and Frank Sanders rode by the family home. Kate and Allen along with the children Maude age 6, Alonzo, age 3, and the baby, Frank, were observed working in the garden. The garden was situated east of the house toward the river and in the shadow of the bluff.

Shortly after John Thompson and Frank Sanders rode past the home, the band of Lipan descended the mountain and began the trek that would eventually be disastrous for not only the McLaurins and Leases but to themselves as well.

The Indians quietly made their way down the mountain and approached the house, knowing full well that safety for the time being was on their side. Curiosity seemed to be their main objective as they dismounted their horses and stealthy approached the yard gate. The Indian woman among them was probably intrigued and excited by Kate's clothing that she found drying on the fence. Inside the house they found the necessities that adorned the cabin quite different from the necessities of their own habitats. Overjoyed by all this, they forgot the family was so near.

Kate heard a sound. Assuming the yard gate had been left open and that the hogs had entered the house, she sent Allen to send the hogs on their way. Allen ran to the house and as he topped the rise he learned all too late exactly what was creating the noise. He turned to call a warning to Kate and was felled by the shot of a Lipan warrior. The shot to his head killed him instantly.

When Kate heard the shot, she screamed for Maude and Alonzo to run. Kate gathered the baby in her arms and was shot as she attempted escape. Maude and Alonzo escaped the confines of the garden fence and as Maude turned back she saw her wounded mother struggling to get over the fence with the baby. Maude returned and took the baby from her mother. With assistance from Maude, Kate managed to get over the fence even though she had been shot five times.

With Kate and Allen, the two elements of danger, out of the way, the Lipans finished plundering the house. They took what items that attracted them and left the McLaurin homestead for Mexico.

Kate collapsed on the other side of the fence. Maude and Alonzo were petrified and the baby was sobbing as his dying, bleeding mother tried to comfort him. Kate knew this was a desperate situation and the only person she had to rely on was six year old Maude. She called Maude to her side and told her she was going to have to go for help. Maude stood and looked south towards help and safety but then she looked at her mother, turned west and headed for the house. The Lipans were shocked to see this young wisp of a girl coming straight towards them. It is possible they might have considered eliminating her life also but perhaps the motherly instinct of the Indian woman stopped them. They stood in respect and awe as Maude took a pillow from her bed and ran back to her mother.

Everyone still wonders about the compassion shown to the young McLaurin children. Some say the young Indian woman of the group was the determining factor in the children being spared.

Kate knew her life was waning but was somewhat comforted by Maude's act of courage. She again instructed

Maude to run to the home of the Fisher's for help. At this
point Maude bade her mother good-bye and ran south. She
found Mr. Fisher at his favorite fishing hole located a short
distance from the home. Maude told him her mom had
been shot by Indians and that she needed help. Mrs. Fisher
was a short distance away. The three proceeded to the
Fisher house for a gun and went from there to the home of
Jim Hicks. Along the way towards the settlement of Leakey
they picked up Henry Wall and Mrs. Goodman. At the Dave
Thompson home they left the two women and young Maude.

Meanwhile, in the secluded valley on the Frio the Lipans
mounted their horses and began their escape to the
mountains of Mexico. Further down stream, John McLaurin
was having concerned thoughts and felt very uneasy about
his wife and family.

As John McLaurin was heading home he saw Jim Hicks.
Jim, who was on his way to warn the Leakey settlement of
the tragedy at John's home, did not recognize John and thus
did not give him the news. John McLaurin next met John
Leakey and the sad news was conveyed. John was assured
that Maude was safe and well cared for at the Thompson
home, for it was there the women had her retell her story
and then tried their best to ease the pain that Maude
suffered from the events of the day.

As the sun sank slowly in the west the men of Leakey
found Kate. It was there on the banks of the Frio River that
John found his dying wife.

In spite of the five gunshot wounds, Kate, out of concern
for the safety of her children, was still barely clinging to life.
And with words of comfort from her husband and a few sips
of water from the brim of his hat, Kate drew her final breath.

A posse of about twenty men gathered to pursue this
small band of Lipan Apache Indians. Eventually the rough
terrain, wet weather and tired horses caused most of the
men to return home. A few continued on the trail to Ft.
Clark where General Bullis and his Black Seminole Scouts

took over the job. They were relentless and would continue after this band until the revenge of the McLaurin and Lease families was final. This group of men played a great role in the taming of the west. Their history is as strong as their culture.

The Black Seminoles that served in the year of 1881 were James Perryman, Ben Wilson, Bill Warrior, John Ward, and John Thompson. Some of these men, along with Teracita a Lipan-Apache woman, were in pursuit of the band of Lipan-Apache that had brought sadness to the Frio Canyon. Teracita was the wife of James Perryman. However, after five days of trailing, Teracita had an uncanny feeling she was leading the Scouts after her own people. It was then, she decided to lead them astray. The scouts soon became wise to her trick. When accused, Teracita became so uncontrollable that she was tied to her horse to keep her from escaping and setting off an alert to the unsuspecting band of Lipan Apache.

Did the Lipan know they were being followed? This is just another one of the questions that will never be answered. But Bullis and his Scouts were relentless and after five more days of tracking they found the Lipans camped at Horseshoe Bend in the mountains of Mexico. Bullis and the Scouts surrounded the camp and after a short battle five warriors and one woman were dead. Another woman and a child were taken captive. The captive woman lost a hand during the fight. It is believed her life may have been spared because she said she kept the band from killing Maude and the rest of the McLaurin children. She and the captive child were sent to the reservation at Ft. Sill.

John McLaurin later identified the clothing and other articles retrieved from the Indians as items that had belonged to his family. This confirmed the Scouts had avenged the deaths of Kate McLaurin and Allen Lease.

The McLaurin Indian raid, as historians describe it, is also known as the last Indian raid in the Frio Canyon and possibly the last in south central Texas. For the Seminole Scouts, the trek into Mexico was their last as well. Bullis gave up his command of the Scouts in 1881. The Seminole Scouts were eventually evicted from Ft. Clark, disbanded and never received the land that was promised them by the U. S. Government. Descendents of the Scouts can still be found in the Brackettville and Del Rio area of Texas.

As for the Lipan Apache, the end of the 19th century left their way of life to history. With their land gone, there was little choice left but to relocate to the Mescalero Reservation in New Mexico. It was here they would live with the rest of the Apache.

The McLaurin family did survive. With the help of his mother and family members, John continued with the care and rearing of his motherless children. He died on October 31, 1935, at the age of eighty.

These few words and pages cannot begin to describe or to explain the lives that were touched by this one event. It is in honor of all the people involved in this story that I dedicate these words, and credit the people who keep this story alive. It is a tribute to them all.

Ghost Stories

The White Lady of Rio Frio

Sometimes along the Frio River, when the night is clear and still, you see what appears to be a woman dressed in white. Then you blink your eyes and the woman is several yards away from where you saw her a moment ago. You rub your eyes and you wonder just what you really saw. Then you remember that it could be the White Lady. Could it be that the White Lady of Rio Frio is just a wisp of river fog? Or does a real ghost haunt the Frio Canyon?

The story of the White Lady stems from a love story that took place during the early 1900s. Maria Juarez and her sister were two of the prettiest *senoritas* in the canyon. Maria's sister was married to Gregorio, a handsome man who worked on one of the ranches located in the canyon. Maria spent many hours at her sister's *casa.* Maria and her sister were very close even though Maria was several years younger.

Maria helped care for her sister's children. She longed for the day when she would be old enough to marry and have children of her own.

As Maria grew older, Gregorio began to notice her beauty but, alas, he was married to her sister. Maria also caught the eye of Anselmo Tobar. Anselmo was a very eligible vaquero who worked on the Patterson Ranch. Anselmo began courting the beautiful Maria. This made Maria so happy for she knew that one day soon she would be married and be able to begin her own family. One day Gregorio called Maria aside and told her of his love for her. Maria scoffed at his words and told him of her love for Anselmo and the plans that they had to one day marry. Gregorio went into a rage scaring the young Maria. Maria ran back to the safety of her home and to await the late evening when Anslemo would come by to visit.

Soon after dark Maria heard a noise outside her home, thinking it was Anselmo she went outside to greet him. She

78

froze in horror as she faced a distraught Gregorio. Panic seized her as she watched him draw a pistol from his belt and point it towards her. She thought she heard a shot but she wasn't sure as the night was slowly turning darker around her.

Maria's dreams died with her that night. There would be no marriage and there would be no children. Her soul could never rest without having experienced the two things that she wanted most from life.

As he stood there looking at the result of the deed he had done, Gregorio heard voices. The sound of the lone shot had echoed the canyon bringing people running. He dropped the pistol and ran to the nearby barn. He hid there behind the hay, not knowing how long he would have to stay. He had no plan. He just knew that he could not share his love for Maria with anyone else. If he could not have her, neither could Anselmo.

A crowd gathered and began a search for the murderer of the beloved Maria. As the sun rose the next morning more men gathered with their guns, horses and hunting dogs. The area was thoroughly searched. The only strong sent that the dogs located was around the home and the barn area. Could it be? Could the murderer Gregorio be in the barn? Cautiously the posse entered the barn. The dogs began to bay and from behind the hay Gregorio arose and gave himself up to the posse. Gregorio raised his hands and walked forward. All the guns were poised on him. He confessed to the murder and swore his love for the beautiful Maria.

Gregorio was tried and sent to prison. Maria was laid to rest in the serene cemetery not far from the Frio River. But her soul is not fulfilled nor at rest. Her spirit still roams the canyon comforting the children in need. She has been known to cover a child on a cold night or to just sit at the foot of the bed as if guarding the child from harm. She is seen dressed all in white as she wanders from place to place.

Many have doubted her sightings. Many swear to her presence. How long will it be before the unhappy soul of

Maria Juarez finds closure? Or will she ever be content? Will she continue to guard the children of the canyon as if they are her own or will she one day no longer appear?

There is no doubt about the love triangle of Gregorio, Maria and Anslemo but is the spirit of the Frio really the white apparition of Maria Juarez or just a cloud of river fog?

Afterword

One wonders if this story is a version of the Mexican folktale *La Llorona (the Sobbing Woman)*. It is a sad tale about a woman who drowns her three babies because a lover did not want to be bothered with the children. She soon was saddened by her deed. Her lover left and she was alone. In her sadness she threw herself in the river at the same spot where she murdered her children. It is now said that she roams the rivers, crying and sobbing. No child is safe along the rivers for if La Llorona sees a child by the river she raises her hand from the water and grabs the child for her own.

Now I don't know about you, but if I was a child you couldn't get me close to the river!

La Llorona

By Zinita Fowler

Don't go down to the river, child,
Don't go there alone;
For the sobbing woman, wet and wild,
Might claim you for her own.

She weeps when the sun is murky red;
She wails when the moon is old;
She cries for her babies, still and dead,
Who drowned in the water cold.

Abandoned by a faithless love,
Filled with fear and hate.
She flung them from a cliff above
And left them to their fate.

Dawn and night, she heard their screams,
Borne on the current's crest;
Their tortured faces filled her dreams,
And gave her heart no rest.

Crazed by guilt and dazed by pain,
Weary from loss of sleep,
She leaped in the river, lashed by rain,
And drowned in the waters deep.

She seeks her children day and night,
Wandering, lost, and cold;
She weeps and moans in dark and light,
A tortured restless soul.

Don't go down to the river, child
Don't go there alone;
For the sobbing woman, wet, and wild,
Might claim you for her own.

Material is taken from a Mexican folktale.

Zinita Fowler is a former Texas teacher and librarian. She is a master storyteller of Texas folk tales and has written three books on Texas ghost stories.

She is a delightful lady who gave me much encouragement and allowed me to use her poem in my book.

El Muerto, The Headless Horseman of Texas

For years I have heard of *El Muerto* but it wasn't until recently that I realized that an ancestor of mine might have had a part in this bone-chilling ghost legend.

Creed Taylor, Texas Ranger and Indian fighter, is an ancestor of mine by marriage. My uncle, Joe D. Tomberlin who is mentioned elsewhere in this book, is a great-nephew of Creed Taylor.

Creed had several brothers, all sons of Josiah Taylor of Virginia, a cousin of General Zachary Taylor. Josiah first came to Texas in 1811. While on this expedition, he was badly wounded. He was able to return to Virginia where his wounds healed. He then came back to Texas in 1820, settling in south Texas around the present town of Cuero. He died there in 1830 leaving the ranch to his widow and sons, Pitkin, Creed, Josiah, William and Rufus. Creed eventually took up his father's wandering ways and ended up around Fort Mason.

The Taylors were a clannish type of people and when wronged would fight to the death of someone, that usually being the opposite party involved in the wrong-doing.

Through the years Creed led an interesting life. Sometimes he served as a Texas Ranger doing everything he could to capture outlaws and fight Indians. And then other times Creed was on the opposite side of the law. He was a contributor in the Taylor and Sutton Feud, one of the great feuds in Texas history. As an older fellow, Creed decided to make his final home in Kimble County, Texas.

It was in Kimble County where he ranched and raised his beloved racehorses. He felt very possessive of his stock and was not lenient with anyone who bothered them.

Now there was this rustler by the name of Vidal who coveted some of Creed's horses. Not realizing that Creed was very possessive of his string of racehorses and mustangs and had the reputation of being a great tracker, Vidal made the sad mistake of just "borrowing" a few for a while.

If Vidal had only known the reputation for tracking that belonged to Creed he would have left that herd of horses alone. Creed, though an old man at the time of the theft, mounted up and began tracking the herd and Vidal, to hell and back if necessary.

From his home in Kimble County, Creed went south, following the Nueces River. The area from Kimble County to south of Uvalde is very hilly and rocky making tracking difficult. But this did not slow or deter Creed Taylor. Creed relentlessly stayed on the trail of Vidal. Somewhere below Uvalde he ran into an old friend and fellow tracker, Big Foot Wallace. What a pair! At this point Vidal's fate was surely sealed and he was doomed to become a part of history and many ghost stories.

Creed and Wallace rode hell-bent for leather after the rustler and the herd of horses. Then one moonlit night they found the rustlers. Patiently they waited until the rustlers were snug in their bedrolls. Then they made their move. Evidently the rustlers were unaware that they were being pursued as they only had one cowboy standing guard on the *remuda*.

Carefully Creed, Wallace and the few other men who had joined in the search surrounded the camp. They were very careful not to alert the lone guard or to spook the horses. Creed called out to the rustlers and as they jumped to their feet they were immediately felled by gunfire. Creed and Wallace located the now dead leader, Vidal. This is where the real tale begins...

There was a reward on the head of this rustler, Vidal. After all he was a notorious *bandito* of the Texas plains but Creed and Big Foot had other ideas for his head. Yep, you

Creed Taylor

guessed it; they cut off his head! Then they caught the wildest mustang from the *remuda*, lashed the headless body to a saddle on the crazed horse. To top it off they put Vidal's hat on the decapitated head and tied the hat and head to the saddle horn. Thus creating a form that still haunts South Texas today.

They turned the mustang loose. To them the fun was just beginning. The pony pitched, bucked and did everything he could to rid himself of this headless rider. Eventually the mustang broke and ran for all he was worth into the *brasadas* and into the legends of South Texas.

Now Creed and Big Foot did this little deed to serve as a warning to others, who might rustle other horses or cattle. Little did they know of the stories that would come from it.

For awhile many cowboys feared the site of *El Muerto*, the headless one. Many shot at the headless body, only to see the crazed mustang bolt and run with the headless form-sitting upright in the saddle with the head bobbing up and down from the saddle horn.

The fear of *El Muerto* continued for quite awhile. The thought, much less the sight, of the headless one made the people of Texas shudder with fear.

The mustang, with it's now mummified and headless rider, was caught one day at a water hole. *El Muerto's* bullet riddled body was removed from the now aged horse and lowered into its final resting spot, a grave near the small town of Ben Bolt. But the body of *El Muerto* has never been able to rest. Like many of the souls that are unable to enjoy their final rest, the legend of *El Muerto*, still roams the South Texas area. At night, sometime in the late evening and, maybe, the early morning you might just catch a glimpse of a small crazed mustang with it's headless rider roaming the Texas landscape. Or could it just be your imagination?

SOMEWHERE IN THE WEST

Old Man Quirt

Back in the 1950s, children in the Frio Canyon would find various ways to entertain themselves. Most of us didn't have a TV and radios were only turned on at the parent's discretion. So we would walk the canyon looking for arrowheads, hunting, fishing, and just letting our imaginations wander.

A favorite fishing hole was located a little south of an old, abandoned, boarded-up house, a house overgrown with weeds. The fence around the house sagged and a loose piece of tin banged with every breath of breeze. In the spring, a lone Mountain Laurel bloomed profusely in the yard, sending its fragrant scent throughout the area.

One late spring evening at about sundown, fishing was slow, and I caught the sweet smell of the Mountain Laurel and decided to follow the scent. As I drew close to the old house I heard what I thought was a gunshot. I eased back behind a bush and drew a slow quiet breath of air. Then I heard the shot again, but this time I also heard voices, voices that hinted of a story from the past. I was too far away to make out what was being said and too scared to move closer. So I went back to the river and got my friend, Greg.

Now Greg was a little skeptical of what I told him. As a matter of fact, he thought I had lost my mind. I managed to convince him to come with me back to the spot. We sat there quietly by the Mesquite bush for a few minutes. We were very quiet, so quiet that as the wind gently blew through the mesquites it sounded almost like a ghostly whisper. Then there it was again. A shot that sounded like it came from a pistol. It was almost dark now and the moon was sending a glow over the top of the mountains announcing that a full moon would soon be arriving. Then a raspy voice was heard, "You mangy critters come out from behind that bush! I see you there and you'll never take me alive!"

87

Was this voice talking to us? We were so afraid that we couldn't move. Then again, "You heard me, come out let me see who you are!"

Well Greg and I crouched closer back against a very thorny Mesquite not knowing exactly what to do. We wanted to run but curiosity and fear kept us there, shivering in our boots.

Another voice was heard, "Come out Quirt! We are tired of you chasing us and we intend to get rid of you! This time for good!"

"Ha! You'll never get me! I am Quirt Fleming with the Frontier District of the San Saba, Texas Ranger Company under Capt. W. R. Wood and you, Sam Bass, are under arrest. I have trailed you from Round Rock where they think you're dead. I am taking you in so step out and make this easy on your self. It is time you and your gang of young scally wags made an honest living."

Another volley of shots rang out! We closed our eyes in fear. As the moon cast an eerie light over the valley a silence fell as if nothing had happened at all.

Greg and I high-tailed it to his grandmother's house and after a severe lecture on staying out so late we told her what we had heard down by the old abandoned house.

Well, she kinda rolled her eyes at us then told us to sit down. Then she began to tell this story. . .

"Now you kids have seen that head stone underneath that lone mesquite in the middle field." We nodded yes and eagerly awaited the rest of her story. "Well, that marks the grave of old John McQuirter Fleming. We all knew him as Old Man Quirt. He always lived alone in that old house. No one ever came to see him so we just figured that he didn't have a family. We kids would always hide in the bushes around the house to watch him because our parents told us that he was crazy and to leave him alone. They said that he claimed he was the Texas Ranger who had shot

Sam Bass and his gang and that he had met Billy the Kid. 'Course they said that he was just telling a windy and that you couldn't believe a thing he said. One day when we were hiding in the bushes watching him, he fell while he was weeding his garden. He couldn't get up so we eased from our hiding place and very gingerly walked up to his garden fence.

"He said, 'I was hoping you kids would come help me. I've knowed you was there many times.'

"Well, all that time the old man had known we had been watching him. We helped him up and then helped him finish his weeding. When we were through, he told us to sit there on the edge of his porch while he got us a cup of cool water. After a few minutes he returned with two tin cups of the coolest water we had ever tasted. He told us the water was so cool because he had channeled the spring, that is located at the ledge behind his house, to run from its shallow basin to the house. He then tunneled the channel underneath the house to a trap door in the kitchen floor. In this way he always had cool water, especially when the house was surrounded by Indians. Well we wondered if this was just another of Old Man Quirt's tales.

"After that first visit we returned to just sit with Old Man Quirt. With each visit we heard another new and exciting story. He would tell us about his life as a Texas Ranger, about bank robbers and about Indians. He told us he had always been alone and never had time to settle down with a wife and kids.

"Our folks just laughed when we told them about our visits with Old Man Quirt. They told us not to believe all that hogwash and that those stories he told were just ones that he made up and that he was just a crazy old man. However, we didn't believe them at all.

"One day, I think it was in the early fall, we went to see Old Man Quirt but when we got there the house was so still and silent. The creak the porch boards made as we walked up onto it sounded so loud. We knocked on the door, but there was no answer. My brother looked in the window and turned to me as his eyes filled with tears."

Grandma wiped a tear from her eye at this point and sighed before she went on with her story. "Brother said to me that it looked like Old Man Quirt was dead. We ran home and Ma called Preacher Smith and Sheriff Garrett. They buried Old Man Quirt out in that middle field. Somebody later planted a Mesquite bush there and put a hand carved headstone over his grave. We never told our folks but it were us kids that did it.

"Before the house was boarded up we went back there to just look around. We had sat many hours on the porch, listening to Old Man Quirt's stories but he had never invited us inside. We gingerly opened the front door. I tell you the squeak of that old door scared us half to death. We were so amazed when we walked around there in the house. We did find that trap door in the kitchen. We opened that trap door and there beneath we found the cool spring water swirling below the floor. But what amazed us the most was the old trunk. It's that one sitting in the corner over there. My brother and I carried it home and I kept it in my room and never showed my folks what was inside but I guess I can open it for you kids."

We opened the trunk that night and its contents brought tears to our eyes. There inside was an old Colt 45, a pair of binoculars with the name Billy Bonney scratched on the side, an Indian arrow, a letter to Sam Bass from his sister, but most importantly of all a Texas Ranger badge.

So, sometimes when the canyon is quiet and as a full moon eases over the mountains, that crack that you heard just might be a pistol shot. The sounds that you hear as a breeze picks up might just be voices from the past. It might not be your imagination at all.

Afterword

This story is based on many facts. My great-great grandfather was John McQuirter Fleming and he was a Texas Ranger. In the Frio Canyon, there is a lone grave underneath a Mesquite tree and an old house, but the grave is not that of John McQuirter Fleming. There is a house there but the house in the story is patterned after The Fleming Springs house in San Saba, which is now owned by Tommy Lee Jones. The Fleming Springs house does have a spring channeled underneath it for the exact reason mentioned in the story. My great-great grandfather Ambrose Smith was a circuit rider Baptist preacher and Pat Garrett was in this area for a time. Billy the Kid is supposed to have cowboyed in the canyon at one time and left a pair of binoculars. Greg and I did go to school together and still swap tales to this very day. Mountain Laurel does bloom here and the full moon does cast an eerie glow on the canyon. Sometimes when the night is still and quiet you might even hear gun shots.

One Texas Ranger Card

```
Name & Rank:Fleming, J. M., Pvt.,
Comm. Off:   Wood, W. R., Capt.,
Organ:       Co.for Precinct No.2,San Saba Cty.,
             2nd Front.Dist.,Maj.G.B.Erath,cmdg.,
Enlist:      TST.
             Feb.6-64 at San Saba;Mus.in Feb.6-
Disch:       64 at San Saba.
Descrip:     Service 14 days at $2,tot.$28.
             Age 30 yrs.
Remarks:     R&F 77; 71; Enr.& Mus.off.W.R.Wood;
   Co.org.under the Act of Dec.15-63;1 MR dtd.Feb.-
   64;1 Pay Roll dtd.Feb.6 to Je.1-64;Appears on-
   ly on Pay Roll dtd.Feb.6 to Je.1-64;Transferred
   Menard Cty.
```

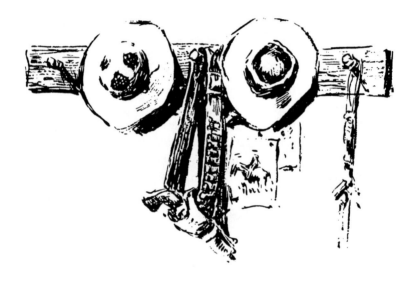

Christmas Poems

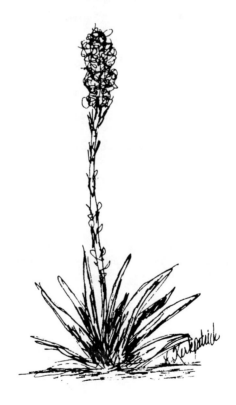

Dear Mr. Saddle-maker,

You know it's close to Christmas time
And I have one big problem here.
I have one request of Santa Claus,
He won't understand, of this I fear.

I'm just a little cowboy
And just turned five you know.
I'm learning how to ride my horse
And to make that pony "whoa."

I've seen what I want many times
In horseman magazines.
All cowboys wear them on their legs,
But I know they're not blue jeans.

So help ole Santa out for me
And tell him what they're called.
I really don't need a very big pair
'Cause I'm still pretty small.

He might put my initials on them.
And fringe of chocolate brown.
So everyone will know me
When I go to town.

So thank you Mr. Saddlemaker
For doing the best you can,
To help this little cowboy out
Till I become a man.

Love, Wade

My oldest grandson, Wade, was about four years old when we were discussing his Christmas wish list. We were on our way to the ranch to feed when he told me that he knew what he wanted but he didn't know exactly what they were called. So I ask him if he could describe what he wanted and this is when he told me the story line that I followed in the poem. Now we just happen to have a good friend, Leo Naumann, who is a saddle maker, so I ordered the gift for Wade in the form of a poem.

Needless to say, Leo was delighted and so was Wade with his gift. Leo has made saddles for my dad and also my son and now, since my dad is retired, Wade is riding his great grandfather's saddle.

Wade, his new chaps, and his cousin, Chelsea.

The Texas Snowman

Kids in Texas have a problem
When Christmas rolls around
They cannot build a snowman
With no snow upon the ground.

Now they've heard 'bout ole Frosty,
Why they sing of him each year
But that stuff that he is made of
Is like the silk purse and sow's ear.

So they gathered a bunch of pictures
And did a net search, don't you know,
And tried their best to figure out
Why Texas has no snow.

The computer kid named Mikie,
Well he made their bubble pop
When he told them that Texas weather
Was simply too darn hot!

So they went to the art department,
Where little Stevie took the show.
He said they would build a snowman
And that they would build it without snow.

"Just bring to me a lot of things,
We will use just what you find.
We will put it all together
And a snowman we'll mastermind."

So they gathered up a lot of things,
But they really did not know
How all of this assorted stuff
Could make Frosty with no snow.

Frankie brought his old guitar,
The one with broken strings
And then he hoped, beyond all hope,
That maybe Frosty could sing!

Joe gathered up his trick ropes,
The ones that wouldn't work.
He left them for that snowman
And his smile had a little quirk

Carroll brought a red plaid vest
And Sue, she brought a bow,
Paul he brought a Stetson hat,
His grand-pa's don't you know.

Kathy brought some overalls,
Billy a pair of boots,
Ronnie brought a piece of board
And Bettie a cheroot.

One by one they piled these things
In a heap upon the ground.
Sure didn't look like a snowman
Then they heard an eerie sound.

Everything got kinda quiet
And the wind began to blow,
And over the hill came a norther
That maybe might bring snow!

The dark sky began to tumble
And round things blew around,
Blowing here and blowing there
As the children stood spellbound!

That norther blew in tumbleweeds
From out West Texas way,
And this is how ole Frosty
Would come to life that day!

Some settled up against the fence,
In an artistic sort of way.
They took the shape of a snowman,
Those tumbleweeds saved the day!

The kids dressed him in the overalls
And he looked cute as pie.
They placed the hat upon his head
And then he winked his eye.

Frosty started two stepping,
Then a schottische and a do-si-do.
He danced and sang around them
And he wasn't made of snow.

So Merry Christmas to you,
And when the wind blows up a gale,
Go out and build your snowman,
Just like in this tall tale!

    "The Texas Snowman" was written about some imaginary kids in Texas. Since it is very seldom Texas kids see snow, they must use their imagination to produce it. I remember as a small child wanting to build a snowman. My mother always told me about the ones that she and her brothers would build on the streets of Philadelphia and I always dreamed of the day when I could build one of my very own. That snowman only happened once in my life when we got a couple of inches of snow. The children in my poem acquired the names of friends.

Santa Claus's Sidekick

Now every cowboy hero had a sidekick
  that was true,
But did you know that Santa Claus,
  well, he had a sidekick, too.

Santa had the sniffles
  and his gout was acting up.
He hated to admit it,
  but he was sicker than a pup.

But the kids from the world all round
  on Santa they did wait.
So he somehow had to hitch his sleigh
  and keep that special date.

Yep, Santa had a problem,
  along with the North Pole flu.
The elves were all too tired to work
  and the reindeer wouldn't do.

So he turned to his computer
  and the whole world he did scan
From the hills and plains of Texas
  to the sands of Pakistan.

Hmmmm, he scanned back there to Texas,
  where he saw a tiny light.
It looked like someone's campfire.
  Could it be? Yep, he was right.

It was the campfire of ole Sour Dough,
  the cook from the Bar U spread.
Shoot, he was so old and cranky,
  that Santa feared that he was dead.

Sour Dough had helped him once before
    when he needed an extra hand.
He might pitch in and help him now
    and ride for Santa's brand.

Santa called him on his cell phone
    and then his nose he blew
"Yea?" answered Sour Dough
    and Santa answered "Sour, how are you?"

"Santa, good to hear you!!
    And what is on your mind?"
"I'm so sick." Wheezed ole Santa,
    "and I'm running far behind."

"I was wondering could you help me
    deliver all these toys.
If you could handle Texas
    and all those girls and boys."

Sour Dough rubbed his scraggly beard
    and scratched his balding head.
"Well certainly, Santa I'll help you out!
    I'll go and hitch up Fred!"

Fred was Sour's tiger stripped mule
    and cranky this mule was!
But Sour would line this mule out
    'cause they must help ole Santa Clause.

With Fred hitched to the chuck wagon,
    they'd meet Santa on the way
And pick up all the toys
    that they must deliver on this day.

Fred kicked the single tree
    and balked a time or two.
He brayed and stomped and twitched his ears
    just like a mule would do.

Then they saw the red light
    as Rudolph led the way
And following was Santa
    and his toy-laden sleigh.

Sour popped his trusty whip
    and hollered out to Fred,
But Fred was planted in his tracks
    just like he was dead.

Sour begged and pleaded
    to that contrary bay equine.
Santa watched this odd dilemma
    and knew that Sour was wasting time.

Santa whistled very softly
   till Fred was hypnotized,
With Fred's attitude adjusted,
   Sour surely was surprised!

Santa sneezed a time or two
   and sprinkled stardust all around;
As Fred, Sour, and the chuck wagon
   slowly left the ground.

It was Sour Dough and Fred
   a flying through the sky
Delivering all the toys
   and leaving smiles you can't deny.

They flew the Texas skies from North to South
   and then from East to West.
Till the chuck wagon was empty
   and Sour needed a rest!

They landed at the bunkhouse
   in the heart of the Bar U Ranch,
Where they heard the sounds of Christmas carols,
   could it be a Christmas dance?

As Sour peeked in through the window,
   he saw much to his surprise,
Old Santy kicking up his heels
   with a twinkle in his eyes!

Well Santa had recovered from the flu
 and was dancing all around!
The bunkhouse rocked with merriment
 and was filled with Christmas sound!

"Thank you Sour for all your help,
 in taking up the slack!
I have something special for you."
 and he reached into his sack!

A sack of stardust he took out
 and handed to Sour Dough.
"Just sprinkle it on that balky mule,
 then whistle soft and low."

"And Merry Christmas Sour Dough,"
 said jolly old Saint Nick.
"And Merry Christmas back at you!"
 said Santa's number one sidekick.

"Santa Claus's Sidekick" was written about a little
problem that Santa encountered. Now my friend, Joe Wells,
has a couple of the most cantankerous mules you have ever
seen. Since I have always given him such a bad time about
his cranky old mules, I decided to cut him a little slack and
make a mule the hero of this story.

The Christmas Story

The kerosene lamp burned brightly all night
    in the window that faced to the south.
A blue norther blew through the cracks in the door;
    the rain would soon end the drought.
He left her early that morning
    to search for that black baldie cow,
That cow always had trouble calving;
    he must sell her someday, somehow.

His wife, she would not worry until sunset
    as the wind still blew up the draw.
It would not warm the entire day
    and the water in the trough wouldn't thaw.
She'd be up all night waiting for him
    while the lamp flickered and the wind blew cold.
She'd lay the Bible on the rickety old table
    to again read the story of old.

They had always read it together,
    the story of the first Christmas Eve,
But tonight she would read it without him,
    as she tried very hard not to grieve.
Then the creak of his saddle awoke her,
    as he put the stray cow in the pen.
She raised her head from the Bible
    and wondered where in the world he'd been.

She built up the fire in the old wood stove
    and brewed coffee in the old porcelain pot.
She heard him merrily call her name
    as he came to the house at a trot.
He bounded up the steps of the weathered old porch,
    as he tried to forget the cold.
He could hardly believe the events of the night,
    a night he would forever behold.

He'd left out early on that Christmas Eve morn,
    headed out towards the Rio Grande.
That old blue norther chilled him to the bone,
    as he rode cross this barren cold land.
He rode all day in search of that cow,
    no telling where she could be,
And then at dusk he found her and her calf,
    sheltered 'neath an old mesquite tree.

As the sun set slowly in the west,
    "Let's head on home," he said.
But they hadn't gone but a mile or two
    when they came to an abandoned old shed.
They'd best stop here and camp for the night
    and get out of this howling gale.
He knew that she'd be worried,
    as that sad old wind did wail.

But wait, what was that noise he heard?
    The wind was now only a sigh.
The stars lit the heavens and desert below
    as he opened the shed door wide.
"*Por favor, Senor*," the young Mexican said.
    "We are lost and don't know the way.
Could we please shelter in your shed tonight?
    You see *mi esposa* needs a place to stay."

"*Seguro que si,*yes, you can!" the cowboy replied.
    "I'd be honored to have you stay.
We'll stoke the fire and warm you up.
    It's been a long, cold, dreary day."
"My name is Jose and this is Maria,"
    the young Mexican said with pride.
"Tonight I fear the babe will come;
    Maria has had a long, long hard ride."

The donkey she rode stood quite still,
    as they helped Maria to the ground.
"*Gracias, gracias!*" he thanked him again.
    His words rang with a heavenly sound.
They fixed Maria a bed made of hay,
    then soon they all went to sleep.
But they awoke to the voice of a shepherd,
    calling softly to his sheep.

The norther outside had stopped blowing,
   the stars were shinning bright.
And there in the manger,
   a baby, born on this holiest, holiest of nights.
Then thundering hooves broke the silence.
   They were unable to say a word.
As out of the darkness came cattle,
   a ghostly stampeding herd.

The herd was followed by cowboys,
   apparitions all clothed in white.
Their saddles were laden with silver;
   they were such a heavenly sight.
The horses they rode were translucent,
   from their hooves lightening did spark.
They came in a luminous whirlwind,
   they made the night no longer seem dark.

They dismounted and approached the manger
   and left their cache on the ground.
They remounted and rode off in silence;
   no one made a sound.
The cowboy finally caught his breath,
   while Jose and Maria did pray.
They thanked the Lord for the baby
   and the gifts they were given this day.

They covered the babe with a poncho,
    even though it was tattered and old.
They knew that it would protect him
    from the wind and the bone chilling cold.
The cowboy awoke the next morning;
    in the night the fire had gone out.
But where were Jose and Maria?
    As silently he looked about.

"Guess I must a' been dreaming," he said
    as he carefully looked around.
He poured the last of his coffee
    on an amber coal on the ground.
He picked up his saddle and blanket
    and as he prepared to go
He noticed lying in the manger
    a tattered and old poncho.

He folded it gently to put in his pack,
    took his saddle and went to the door,
He then saw the note that was tacked to a post,
    "*Muchas gracias* forever, *Senior*."
He thought of his life here in Texas,
    he thought of his wife at home,
He knew she was worrying about him;
    he knew she was cold and alone.

He pointed the cow and calf north,
　　if he hurried he could make home soon.
If they didn't have any problems,
　　he could be at his table by noon.
The lamp in the window would welcome him
　　and happily he called her name.
The wind was beginning to die down
　　then he noticed the flickering flame.

He told her of his wondrous night
　　and when her doubts began to show,
He opened his pack on the table
　　and unfolded the tattered poncho.
They knew a miracle had happened
　　as it had many years before.
They opened the Bible before them
　　and read the story again once more.

　　"The Christmas Story" is an imaginary story of
Christmas. It began with a childhood memory. I
remembered we could never go anywhere or do anything
until all the chores were done, stock fed and accounted for.
The poem, "The Christmas Story," like a couple of my
others, just took off on its own and ended up about
Christmas.

'Twas The Night Before
Christmas at the Sansom Ranch

'Twas the night before Christmas and out in the barn
The goats started kidding and this ain't no yarn.
Now Sonny was sitting inside of the house,
Another night wondering where was his spouse?

His wet boots were sitting outside by the door
And Bettie's were on her—need I say more.
The dogs were all quiet, they'd just been fed
The cattle were bedded down by the shed.

Sonny turned back the covers and climbed in the sack
While Bettie curled up beside the haystack.
When out in the pasture, close to the river,
Came the strangest of noises. The kind that make you all quiver.

Sonny ran to the door adoning his jeans,
And hollering for Bettie as he stared at the gleam.
The moon was full that glorious night,
As a matter of fact he'd never seen it so bright.

But there at the gate and headed his way
Was a jolly round man in an unusual sleigh.
His team was led by a steer maverick.
"Hurry Bettie Ruth! You're missing St. Nick!"

They pawed and pranced every which way
And damn near threw Nick outa that sleigh!
"Now Baldy! Now Blackie! You cancer eyed cows!
You'd better shape up or I'll trade you for sows!"

"Let's go to the barn and stop by the pens,
I swear one day I'll trade you for hens!"
On that cold clear night they appeared to fly
As they bounced St. Nick around in the sky.

They finally stopped; he gave a sigh of relief
Those darned ole heifers caused him too much grief.
Sonny saw them all in the brilliant moon glow
He called out to Bettie, "Hey, You're missin' the show!"

That little ole man in his worn suit of red
Pulled a bag from his sleigh and went to the shed.
He walked kinda funny in his pointed toed boots;
Could it be Mac Gilliat down by the chutes?

Of course it couldn't but he must be dreaming
Now where's Bettie Ruth and what is that ringing?
Santa came from the shed with his eyes all aglow
His cheeks were quite rosy and he swayed to and fro.

His mouth was all puckered like he'd ate a cherry.
Sonny couldn't believe this elf was so merry!
He patted ole Baldy and looked in her eye
He mumbled and stumbled and fell in cow pie.

He rolled on the ground and crawled to his team;
Sonny couldn't believe it, this must be a dream!
Again he called Bettie and grabbed for his coat
He couldn't believe it, Santa was stealing a goat!

Sonny grabbed ole Santa before he got in his sleigh.
Three seconds later and he'd been on his way!
The ringing he heard was the old lead goat's bell
He was in Santa's sack, he could tell by the smell!

He grabbed the sack and to Santa he said,
"What's got into you and stay outa my shed!"
"Now hold on there Sonny!" was Santa's reply
"We needed a break, we were too tired to fly!"

"And what is your answer, you lowly coyote?
Don't make no excuses, why'd you steal my lead goat?"
"Now settle down Sonny, here have a chew,
I needed a goat for Christmas Bar B Q!"

Sonny was stunned. What should he do?
Should he deprive Santa of a Goat Bar B Q?
Sonny scratched his head and gave it some thought
Then said, "All right Santa this goat you just bought."

Now Santa was happy as happy could be
And boarded his sleigh with his little goat—ee.
He whistled and cursed but the cows moved not
So he dug in his bag for his trusty hot shot!

So Blackie and Baldy took off in the sky
Leaving Sonny looking and wondering why.
Sonny had to find Bettie and tell her the news
It was then that he found her taking a snooze.

Bettie's convinced that he had a bad dream
Or maybe he'd eaten too many beans!
No one believed him, not even a few
His tale of ole Santa and the Goat Bar B Q!

I guess that every poet has to write a take on "'Twas the Night Before Christmas" and so have I. Again the names of friends have been used as the characters and to protect innocent people.

Sonny and Bettie are friends of mine. Sonny is the County Judge of Real County, Texas, and Bettie is a teacher at Leakey ISD. They raise registered Angora Goats. Beginning in December and January the mama goats have their babies. An Angora kid is usually weak when it is first born and on cold nights ranchers spend many hours in the barn making sure that each kid born gets a tummy full of warm milk to get them off to a good start. And this job is usually Bettie's! Mac Gilliat is a retired County Agent and we have constantly teased him about the pointed toed boots that he wears. And down in Texas, bar b q goat is a delicacy!

Poems and History of the Kirkpatrick Family

I was introduced to the song "Let the Rest of the World Go By" when I was very young. It was a popular song around the time of World War II.

My dad, who is from Texas, was stationed in Philadelphia, Pennsylvania, for a time. It was in Philadelphia where he met my mother who worked for the Stetson Hat Company. Seems that she was destined to come west since she worked for the company who made the hat that won the west. They fell in love; she recorded "Let the Rest of the World Go By" for him to play while he was overseas. They married when the war was over and moved to Texas. This area of West Texas is sixty miles from the nearest town, no electricity, no running water in the house, no indoor facilities, no phone—West Texas. My mother said her mom would cry every time she heard "Let the Rest of the World Go By." If my grandmother had only known what challenges faced my mother, she probably would have been panic stricken.

My grandmother didn't come to Texas for a year or so and was she shocked when she arrived. She had to adjust to the desolate ranch and ranch house. The sounds, I am sure, were quite different. Just imagine the hustle and bustle of Philadelphia compared to the sounds of a very isolated ranch. My dad added to the stress of her adjustment by putting an old broom handle by her bed. He told her she needed to run it between the sheets before she retired for the night. By doing this she would be able to remove all the rattlesnakes that hid between the coolness of the sheets! Somehow, she survived her visit to Texas. After my grandmother's stay at the ranch she returned to Philadelphia realizing that my mom and dad were building their "sweet little nest, somewhere in the West."

Before my mom and dad tied the knot, they made a train trip to Texas from Philadelphia. My mom needed to meet the family and to scope out the situation. Being the perfect lady, on her first trip to Texas, she exited the train in a pair of Jodhpurs! How embarrassing! Glad I wasn't around at that time! But she was just the typical gal from the city on her first visit to this romantic place called Texas.

My grandmother Kirkpatrick was a wonderful lady and a perfect hostess. When nature called, my grandmother pointed my mom to the "outhouse." Now my mother, being from the city where her home had all the conveniences was probably shocked beyond words, but the worst was yet to come. Easing down the path towards this small building that was located just a short distance behind the house, one can only wonder what was going through the mind of the outgoing little city girl. This one-hole facility even had a quarter moon carved out of the rickety door. My mom carefully turned the small piece of wood (the lock) that was secured loosely to the door and this allowed her to enter the "outhouse." I am sure her shock caused her to close the door a little too hard and that same little piece of wood fell into place on the outside capturing her in the "outhouse" for a time. Well, first she cried, then she prayed, then she got an idea. She remembered she had a comb in her pocket so she stuck the comb through the crack (I never did see an outhouse that was air tight and probably for good reason) and lifted the latch. She was so embarrassed and she would not tell anyone what had happened. My dad finally got the whole story from her on their way back to Philadelphia. Rumor has it he laughed for miles.

Elizabeth Thompson Kirkpatrick and Paint

My mother couldn't resist those wide-open spaces. She and my dad got married in June of 1944. The lure of the West brought my mother and dad back to Texas after the wedding and after World War II.

My mother learned to cook on a wood stove, to read by kerosene lamp, to haul water to wash in a wash pot outside, and to bathe in a number two tub.

Clarinda Smith Taylor

Texas also lured my great-great grandmother Clarinda Smith Taylor from her long-time home in Butler County, Alabama. Her story is one right out of the pages of *Gone with the Wind.* The War Between the States took its toll on Clarinda and her family. Her husband, a farmer and plantation owner, and three sons marched away to war. Thus leaving Clarinda to manage the plantation, three daughters and two younger sons.

My grandparents, Burl and Clemmie Kirkpatrick and their matched team, Selem and Dilcey

At the end of the war, Clarinda anxiously awaited the return of her husband, Alexander and two of her sons. Her wait was futile for only one son returned. The carpetbaggers closed in on Clarinda causing her to make the serious decision to leave her home in the Deep South. She packed the remains of their family goods, boarded a boat with her children and came to Texas. This had to have been a very trying time for her but one that proved her strength. She was met somewhere along the coast of Texas by her brother. Her younger son, Daniel Hix Taylor, was to become my great grandfather.

Clarinda died never knowing what happened to her husband. It was I who was destined to uncover this "cold case" mystery. Her husband, Alexander Taylor, was captured at Spottsylvania during the Battle of the Wilderness. He died in a prisoner of war camp in Elmyra, New York.

Burl, Old Blue and Tip, the Border Collie

My dad, Alton Kirkpatrick and Paint

Alton Kirkpatrick on Old Blue, holding an Angora goat

My uncle, Lloyd Kirkpatrick, clowning as usual. His wife, Dawn, the inspiration of the poem, Vaquero's Goodbye.

Below: My uncle, Joe D. Tomberlin

*Above: My son,
Douglas Brice on
the right riding
Dunny.*

*At right: The
youngest cowboy,
my grandson
Wade Brice on
Rooster.*

The Cowgirl

I was just a little cowgirl
    of maybe two or three
And tired of riding horses
    upon my Daddy's knee,
He gave me this stick horse
    and for hours I would ride,
Chasing imaginary dogies with
    my collie dog by my side.

I toddled out behind my Dad
    'cause I thought I was a hand,
Just a regular 'ole cowpuncher
    riding for his brand.
But Dad was awful excited,
    he had something for me to see,
There saddled up behind the barn
    was this good paint mare for me.

The saddle we had was way too big,
    for I was pretty small,
But Daddy told me not to fret,
    this was no problem "a'tall."
He took two old worn stirrups
    and laced them to a girt,
Then tied them to the saddle horn
    and I sat there pretty pert.

He then tied the old split reins
    into a hard fast knot,
Just so I wouldn't lose them
    when we began to trot.
I began that day to tag along
    wherever Dad would go;
I was finally a cowgirl
    and my heart was all aglow.

Well, I grew to fit the saddle
    and to rein without the knot,
I even got a faster horse,
    'cause Paint would only trot.
We'd ride up in the mountains
    rounding up the goats and sheep.
We'd ride all day from dawn to dusk,
    then unsaddle, feed and sleep.

And now I am much older
    and I still run the ranch;
My Dad will come and help me out
    when he has the chance.
I gather the cows in a pickup truck,
    with modern pens at hand
And sometimes my love of ranching
    is hard to understand.

Then I gaze at my first stirrups
    hanging on the living room wall
And they remind me of that time
    when I was very, very small.
The life of a cowgirl in Texas
    is what I chose to lead
And all cowgirls in Texas
    are of a very special breed.

We are everywhere in the state
    from the Red to the Rio Grande.
So please, whenever you see us,
    come over and shake our hand.
You'll find a very tender lady
    underneath our skin of brown,
And on our heads a well worn hat
    that we wear just like a crown.

We are the real hearts of Texas
    with a will you can't deny.
Our hearts and souls belong to God
    until the day we die.
So when you speak of Texas
    do not leave these thoughts unsaid,
And remember all us cowgirls,
    we're Texas born and bred.

At the ripe old age of three I began riding a paint mare who was affectionately named "Old Paint." I remember as a young child I always wanted to know why she was called "Old Paint" because at the time I began riding her, she was only five or six years of age. Horses like Paint were the original baby-sitters on a ranch. It made no difference how hard I kicked or how many times I swung my quirt ('course all I ever hit was the saddle skirt), Paint would only walk and every once in a while would trot for two or three steps. A young child mounted on one of these horses was perfectly safe. The child was too high off the ground to get off (as if they wanted to) and being on the horse, they were out of the way of the work that was taking place. Horses like her have an uncanny sense of knowing that a child is aboard because I have seen these same horses become a top ranch horse when someone other than the child was in the saddle. "Old Paint" died on the ranch at the age of 32.

I can remember well Daddy taking an old girth and attaching a pair of small stirrups to each end then tying them to the saddle horn of my child size saddle because the child size saddle was just too big for a three year old rider. I thought that my dad had discovered something special with this contraption, but last fall I saw a painting in Ruidoso, New Mexico, of a young child sitting in a small saddle with this same contraption tied to the saddle horn. It is amazing what a Dad will do to have his young'un tag along.

A single roping rein was unheard of on the ranch, so in order to keep me from dropping the reins; Daddy would tie a knot in them. It also taught me how much slack to give the mare 'cause I got in real trouble if I didn't hold the knot.

Many cowgirls and cowboys got their start in much the same way, tagging along behind their dad on a baby-sitter horse. This poem was one of 8 *Seconds* winners in the Bar D Poetry Contest announced November 17, 2000, at www.cowboypoetry.com.

Linda, at five years old, on Paint.

Linda's daughter Amanda and Fireball

I remember that somewhere there is a line about cowgirls and the love that they have for their horses, and I guess that love just passed from me right on down. The picture above is of my daughter Amanda and her second horse Fireball. Fireball's name was very deceiving. I can remember her crying at the tender age of four, "Fireball won't run!" Fireball seemed to understand that he was to care for her because as she got older he got faster.

On the next page, my granddaughter, Chelsea, riding her Uncle Doug's horse Digger, carries on the family tradition.

Amanda's daughter Chelsea and Digger
Below: Amanda's son Brice on the tractor

The Saga of Lucy Murdock

Once upon a time in Texas,
    where the sage and cactus grow,
Where it is hot as hell in daytime,
    but at night cool breezes blow.
Comes the story of a lady
    and her perilous life on the plain,
Where rattlesnakes and mesquite
    are more common than the rain!

Lucy and Alex Murdock came here
    to settle and make their home.
They tilled the soil and milked their cow,
    vowing never more to roam.
Alex and Lucy worked from dawn to dusk
    improving their little spread.
They built a house and fenced the place
    and put up a lean-to shed.

The house they built was pretty plain,
    just a dog trot with a roof of tin,
When it rained you wouldn't believe
    how much water would come in.
But Lucy did her very best
    to make this house a home,
Amid rattlesnakes and scorpions
    but towards disaster she was prone.

Lucy raised a brood of chickens
　　and milked a Jersey cow,
She planted a kitchen garden
　　and at times she'd even plow.
She always sold her extra eggs
　　and sold her Jersey cream,
She contributed to their coffer
　　or though it so did seem.

Now every Saturday Lucy went to town,
　　kinda like a social call
She dressed up in her very best
　　and donned her tatted shawl.
And with five gallons of Jersey cream
　　and at a very early hour
Lucy Murdock set out for town
　　before the cream could sour.

The buggy mare, named Katy,
　　was in a family way,
So Lucy's trip by that was doomed
　　since she couldn't take that bay.
Alex hitched up their younger mare
　　with instructions to hold her tight.
He assured the reluctant Lucy
　　that the young mare would be all right.

So Lucy got her ample figure
    up in the wagon seat.
Then she set the can of cream
    between her tiny feet.
Alex gave a word of caution
    as Lucy started on her way,
As he didn't have much confidence
    in that prancing little gray.

The gray was a little nervous
    but so far behaved quite well.
But when Lucy let her guard down,
    the trip went all to hell.
They had almost made the second mile
    when a strange noise they did hear,
The sound of a horseless carriage,
    coming right on from the rear!

The gray mare tensed
    and laid back her ears
    at this unfamiliar noise.
Lucy held the skittish mare
    and tried to keep her poise.
The horseless carriage came right on,
    Lucy tried to control the mare,
But I must tell you here and now,
    this was a panicked pair.

The auto car did clatter by,
    the gray did snort and rear;
Lucy tried to prepare herself
    and tried to contain her fear.
The mare's trot became a gallop;
    Lucy reined to no avail.
And as they tore over rutted roads,
    the cream sloshed in the pail.

Lucy's hat blew off her head,
    the cream sloshed all about,
Building pressure inside the can
    that would soon someway come out.
The pressure caused the lid to pop
    and where her hat had been,
A dollop of cream ran through her hair
    and the young mare reared again.
The banging lid was held by wire
    to the handle of the can.
The noise it made scared them more
    as down the road they ran.

Over the hill and around the bend went Lucy,
    the mare and the cream.
Over the bumps, the rocks and ruts
    and did she ever scream.
Slowly she got the wagon stopped
    and breathed a sigh of relief
The mare cooled down and behaved herself
    way beyond belief.

Lucy was not surprised to find
    as a result of the wild run
In the can instead of Jersey cream,
    she found the butter had come.
All the people stopped and stared
    as Lucy arrived in town
The grocer bid her, "Morning Ma'am,"
    and carefully helped her down.

Lucy was so embarrassed,
    but she held her head up high,
She got her butter and her eggs
    and hoped that he would buy.
The grocer bought the butter
    and the eggs that did survive,
And Lucy was just thankful
    to be going home alive.

Alex could not believe her tale
    except for her disheveled state.
But this is not the end of the story
    or the end of Lucy's fate.
Alex took Lucy to the barn
    and much to her surprise
There in the corner of Katy's stall
    was a wonder for her eyes.

You see, Katy had a dun filly
    as yellow as they came;
There was no doubt in Lucy's mind:
    Butter would be her name.

This poem became the composite of a story I once read in an Old West magazine and incidences that happened to my mother, myself plus my imagination. The real Lucy lived on the plains in the 1920s and I took her story and wove these other memories into the rhyme.

I grew up around rattlesnakes and scorpions and to this day the sight of a scorpion makes me shudder. We always had a milk cow, Ducky and Ruby, to name a few. Every Saturday morning I was given the chore of churning the cream that my mom had saved up during the week. The cream she saved was the most disgusting looking curdled mess that I had ever seen! She would skim the cream from the jars of milk and ladle it into this green pitcher. I never liked cream and fresh milk seemed to have more than its share that was always floating to the top of my glass. I would spend several minutes with a spoon trying to get rid of the last tiny specks of that stuff! To top everything off I wasn't really fond of churning, but my mom had a way of convincing me that I would do the job. As a child I also had to care for the chickens. Every week I would clean and carton the eggs to sell without much mishap. Well, except for one Saturday when the handle to the egg basket broke and most of the eggs ended up on the floor with shells scattered all around and the yolks slipping here and there. My profit for the week gone.

Tatting is a needlework that has always fascinated me. I never learned the art but I liked the sound of the word so I decided that Lucy would have a tatted shawl. Since Lucy was trying to control a runaway horse it was only natural that her hat would blow off her head.

My Daddy was always overly cautious to the extent that I was a little scared every time I rode a new horse. So Alex took on this role of my dad. Even though he was a little worried he never let Lucy know that taking the young mare might be a bad idea.

Horses have always had strange ways of being named. Many a cowboy has named a horse based on things that happen as the young horse is being broke to ride. The young horse in this poem got her name in a little different way.

The Vaquero's Goodbye

The air was hot and humid
    on that clear South Texas day
When we gathered at the churchyard,
    our last respects to pay.
There beneath an old mesquite,
    far removed from all the rest,
Stood an old *vaquero*
    dressed up in his Sunday best.

He silently stood there reminiscing
    of all the days gone by;
So many *compadres* had passed on ahead,
    sadness showed weathered eyes.
As we walked on into the chapel
    at a slow and weary pace,
The back of my mind was haunted
    by the look on the *vaquero's* face.

When we were seated
    I saw him standing alone at the rear,
And then slowly he moved forward
    to pay his respects at the bier.
His shirt was of homespun cotton,
    his *chapaderos* had a well-worn hue,
His gnarled hands held his *sombrero*,
    his boots were not quite new.

The moment of silence was broken
    by a heavenly sound that we heard
The whisper of the rowel of his silver spurs,
    silencing the unspoken word.
The fringe on his brown *chapaderos*
    rustling with a softening sigh,
The tapping of his boots giving answer
    to the unanswered question "Why?"

Then in our awe-struck moment,
    we suddenly came back to life
As the sun through the stained glass window
    ended our feelings of strife.
The *vaquero* was bathed in colors
    that filtered softly through the pane
And as he approached the casket
    we knew her death had not been in vain.

Slowly he knelt before her
    in salute of her life and her death,
And then he began to speak
    as all of us held our breath.
"Adios y vio con Dios,"
    the old vaquero sighed,
"El le dio la bendicion."
    He blessed the day that she died.

He then placed a rose on her coffin
    as a final salute to her,
But before he left he gave her
    a gift of his silver spurs.
With the sign of the cross he bid her farewell,
    then turned and walked away
He knew in his heart, his mind and his soul
    they'd meet on another day.

Her grave, now covered in bluebonnets,
    is shaded by a cottonwood
And in that tree a mourning dove coos,
    just like he knew it would.
And sometimes you can hear him
    as the breeze blows through the trees,
In a tired voice he whispers,
    "*Vida las palomas, son como las angles.*"

Spanish to English Translations:

Adios y vio con Dios
    Goodbye and go with God
El le dio la bendicion
    He is giving blessing of her day of death
Vida las palomas, son como las angles.
    Fly with the doves, they are like the angels.

This poem haunted me for several years. I wrote it in memory of my aunt, Dawn Kirkpatrick. Dawn was a rancher's daughter and a rancher's wife. At early morn you could find her in the pens at shearing time and at noon preparing a hearty meal for everyone. When her two children got older, she took a bookkeeping job at the local livestock auction barn to help supplement the income from the ranch. She worked at the auction many years and became a good friend to everyone, from the ring men and pen hands who worked there, to the patrons of the ring. Then sadly it was discovered that the headaches she was experiencing were the result of a brain tumor.

The auction barn is where local ranchers gather to sell their livestock and to visit with each other. For me a few hours at the livestock auction barn was always the highlight of a trip to Uvalde. As Uvalde is located some 55 miles from the ranch, these trips were always a special event. While my dad would drink coffee, visit and watch the sale, I was up on the catwalk listening to the cadence of the auctioneer and looking at all the animals that would soon be finding new homes. I would always pretend that I was a rancher there to buy livestock to take back to my imaginary ranch.

Many people from all walks of life attended Aunt Dawn's funeral. As I was sitting in the family room at the funeral home, I noticed an older Mexican man whom, I assumed had worked with her at the auction–probably in the pens, approach her casket. He knelt, blessed himself and said a prayer. I realized at this time that she had touched so many people and in so many ways. Knowing my Aunt Dawn like I did, she had probably made this man feel as important as the owner of the sale barn. She was that type of person, always ready to listen and to help anyone. The picture of this man honoring her froze in my mind. It was around this scene that I wrote the poem.

The Rose

The rose he left at her gravesite
Has now shattered and blown away.
Yet he continues to go there
He visits her most every day.

He talks to her in the moonlight,
And sometimes in the morning rain,
He does this because he loved her
And it somehow it eases the pain.

The crags in his face grow deeper,
His hair has turned mostly white.
The gait of his walk is much slower.
He wishes she were here tonight.

As slowly he walks to the river
He knows that he too soon will die.
He gazes at the water and smiles
At the rose that passes him by.

God's Greatest Little Cowboy

Have you ever wondered
About the twinkle in the Texas stars at night?
Have you wondered how they got there
Or why they shine so bright?

The answer to the question
Isn't really hard to find,
But sometimes the answer's difficult
And sometimes seems unkind.

You see, God's home is a mansion,
It spreads for miles and miles.
Why it's twice as big as Texas
And it's full of Texas smiles.

Now God loves to keep his mansion bright
With the moon and all the stars
To remind us all of his great love
That is with us near and far.

But sometimes he finds a corner
That the angels failed to light,
And he immediately starts looking
For a special one so bright.

It is very hard to understand
The decision that he will make,
Or why he gives us such a job,
One so hard to undertake.

But as you gaze up in the sky
On a starry moonlight night
Your will notice there's a special glow
On a new star shinning bright.

This star has a special twinkle
And a sparkle that can't compare
He is such a joy, this new little star,
And God is very glad he's there.

And when God needed a cowboy
To ride His range in the sky,
And to keep an eye on his dogies
He knew on Marc he could rely.

He gave him a steed named Comet,
A horse that is faster than light,
And sometimes you can see them
As they ride the range in the night.

So don't wonder about the twinkle
Or why the stars are bright.
Just say a prayer and thank the Lord
'Cause Marc is shinning bright tonight.

Marc's having a great time in heaven,
His heart is filled with joy.
He has a new saddle, boots and spurs:
He's God's Greatest Little Cowboy.

This is the first cowboy poem that I ever wrote. I work at the school in Leakey, Texas, and one of our teachers had this little boy, Marc, who didn't want to be anything but a cowboy. The last time that I saw Marc he was peeking over the divider in my office asking me "Whacha' doin'?" I remember Marc always wore his older brother's hand me down boots that were about two sizes too big. In my memories of him I can see and hear him clunking down the sidewalk in his big brother's boots. We lost Marc to an accident the afternoon before my birthday. The next morning I got up and wrote the poem in his memory.

Marc Grissom

The Little Cowboy's Prayer

Dear God, this is my prayer before I go to sleep,
Can I just talk with you awhile,
Instead of counting sheep?

God, please bless this things that are special to me.
My mom, my dad, my lariat rope,
And especially bless Thee.

Bless my friends, my horse, my dog and my cat.
Bless my saddle, spurs, and don't forget
To bless my brand new hat.

Dear God, are you a cowboy?
Can you make that eight second ride?
Do you ride with all the cowboys when they say "Outside!"?

Thanks for helping with my reading, and especially my math!
And God, please tell my mom
That cowboys don't take baths!

Cow Parts

It's been around for quite awhile
And the cowboy rightly knows,
The one thing that it isn't
Is pleasant to your nose!

It does begin in several ways
And let me tell you friend,
The preliminary stage is what you want
And not the final end.

Now in stage one you find it
Just a lovely blooming flower
But from its bed this bovine beast
Will certainly devour.

This flower is then transformed
Into a succulent rare steak
When cooked over a smokie campfire
Why I'll certainly partake.

But then we have what's left you know
And it's know by many a name
So now you'll hear my story
And how it came to fame.

The garden thrives and grows quite nice
And I guess by now you figure,
Just how manure can add so much
To a garden that is so meager.

When labeled dung, the cowboy knows
It'll make a nice hot fire
For him to sit around at night
His poetry to inspire.

But sometimes it's sorta liquid,
Especially in the chute.
And many a cowboy's wondered
Just why a cow must "toot"!

It is used in cowboy contest
To measure throwing skill
And remember it's what's left over
From the fragrant daffodil!

Some will call it cow pie,
Some will say cow chip
If your feminine, it's patty
But most just say cow _ _ _ _!

So next time you see a bovine
A grazin' in that bower
Kindly just remember
What will happen to that flower!

And when next time you cut into
That nice rare juicy steak
Remember what it could be
And order Rattlesnake!

This poem was a "betcha can't write a poem in five minutes." Being one that can't pass up a dare well as you can see I should have passed up this one!!

The Cuttin' Chute

As the cowboy works the cuttin' gate
There's a few things he's gotta know.
The first and foremost of these things
Is what must stay and what must go.

Now take that ole cow over there
The black with mottled face,
Why she ain't calved in more than a year;
She's got no business on this place.

So I'll just cut her to the left
When she hits the cuttin' gate,
So far of all the cows to go
She'll be number eight.

But when it comes to friends I know
And life is kinda in a tight.
There is one thing fer darn sure,
I'll cut you to the right.

Chili

This poem is dedicated to all my friends who cook chili.

My chili is known throughout the land
And some folks say it's even grand.

But some folks scream and run for cover
And one gal fed it to an X-lover.

My chili is known for its resources,
It'll cure your cold and it's good for horses.

It'll take the rust right off your pan
And the fleas on your dog will up and scram!

Now last year I didn't just sit like a dope,
I cooked Karl's chili while he spun rope.

And Amelia's chili lacked style and grace,
And one would wonder how it won first place!

Chili should always be full of fire
And not sit there like a deflated tire.

So if you want real chili that is nice and hot
Well, come on by, and sample my pot!

But if chili for sissies is what you desire,
Then pass me by for another cook's fire!

I really do cook competition chili. I am not a real serious chili cook but I do enter one or two competitions a year. I have even won a few trophies at local chili cook-offs. These winnings are thanks to Charles and Jo Ann Brice who gave me my first recipe. So if you like hot chili try this altered old family recipe. To pass the time while my chili is cooking, I usually make a dutch oven peach cobbler. So get-out your oven and give the peach cobbler a try.

Cow Camp Chili

3–5 pounds of lean beef, chili ground
1 large onion, chopped fine
3–5 beef bullion cubes in 2 cups hot water
6 + tablespoons chili powder
3 teaspoons cumino
¼ teaspoon oregano
¼ teaspoon red pepper
½ teaspoon paprika
½ teaspoon dried ground jalapeno
¼ teaspoon garlic powder
1 teaspoon fresh fine chopped cilantro
¼ teaspoon liquid smoke
2–3 small cans tomato sauce
salt to taste
pepper to taste
1 or 2 whole canned jalapenos
salsa

Salt and pepper meat. Sauté the onions in a small amount of lard. Add meat and brown. Add broth and 1–2 cups water, bring to boil and simmer about 20 minutes. Add about 3 tablespoons of the chili powder, the seasonings, 1 can of tomato sauce, and 2 tablespoons salsa. Simmer 1 hour. Add chili powder 1 tablespoon at a time to taste. Add the rest of the seasonings as needed and the rest of the tomato sauce. Cook until chili is thick. About 2 or 3 hours start to finish.

Cow Camp Peach Cobbler

4–5 large cans peaches
1 cup of sugar
½ cup brown sugar
dash of cinnamon
½ teaspoon nutmeg
¼ cup flour
½ stick butter

Drain juice from peaches and save. Mix some of the juice with the flour to make a smooth paste. Continue adding the juice to the flour paste until the mixture is smooth. Then add the sugars, cinnamon, nutmeg and the peaches.

Melt ½ stick of butter in the heated dutch oven. Add peach mixture. Top with a lattice crust. Bake in dutch oven very slow to allow the crust to brown. Takes about 30 to 45 minutes and maybe an hour.

Crust

2 cups flour
1 cup shortening
½ cup water
1 teaspoon salt

Cut the above dry ingredients until well mixed, then add the water. Mix by hand on a floured board. Let the dough rest about 15, 20 minutes. Roll dough out on a floured board and cut in thin strips. Cover top of cobbler with strips. Sprinkle sugar and cinnamon on top of crust along with tiny chips of butter.

159

Bibliography

The stories and poems that I have written in this book have been seriously researched. Some of the information also has to be credited to oral history that was handed down to me since I was a child. I hope that the documentation that I have listed here cover as much of the historical and verbal accounts that notes and memory allow.

The Saga of Lucy Murdock

Printed Material:
    Margie M. Lute, "*The Boy, the Butter, and the Runaway Horse*"

The White Lady of Rio Frio

Oral Stories:
    Juan Albarado
    Lance Blazek

El Muerto

Printed Material:
    James T. DeShields, "*Tall Men with Long Rifles*"
    Walter Prescott Webb, "*The Texas Rangers*"
    A. J. Sowell, "*Early Settlers and Indian Fighters of Southwest Texas*"
    Znita Fowler, "*Ghost Stories of Old Texas*"
    Ed Syers, "*Ghost Stories of Texas*"
World Wide Web:
    Wallace L. McKeehan, "*Sons of DeWitt County*"
Family Stories:
    Joe D. Tomberlin

The Plight of Mary Millsap

Printed Material:
    Mike Kingston, "*A Concise History of Texas*"
    Lon Tinkle, "*13 Days to Glory*"
World Wide Web:
    Wallace L. McKeehan, "*Sons of DeWitt County*"
    Julia R. IngleSchultz, "*Isaac Millsap*"

Oral Stories:
  Shonda Brice

Widows of the Alamo

Printed Material:
  Crystal Sasse Ragsdale, *"Women and Children of the Alamo"*
  John Jakes, *"Susannah of the Alamo"*
  Lon Tinkle, *"13 Days to Glory"*
  Mike Kingston, *A Concise History of Texas"*
World Wide Web:
  Sons of DeWitt County
  Handbook of Texas—Online
  Julia R. IngleSchultz, *"Isaac Millsap"*

Cynthia Ann Parker

Printed Material:
  Mary Beth Watson, *"The Squaw with Blue Eyes"*
  Bill Neely, *"The Last Comanche Chief"*
  Jack C. Ramsay Jr., *" Sunshine on the Prairie"*
  Margaret Schmidt Hacker, *"Cynthia Ann Parker, The Life and the Legend"*
  Mrs. Rachel Plummer, *"Narrative of the Capture and Subsequent Sufferings of Mrs. Rachel Plummer"*
  Mike Kingston, *"A Concise History of Texas"*
World Wide Web:
  Dana Stubbs, *"Cynthia Ann Parker"*
  "Handbook of Texas—Cynthia Ann Parker"
  Quanah Chamber of Commerce, *"Medicine Mounds"*

Cathay Williams

World Wide Web:
  Cynthia Savage, *"Female Buffalo Soldier"*
  DeAnn Blanton, *"Excerpt from Minerva, A Quaterly Report on Women and the Military"*
Oral Stories:
  Gwendolyn A. Quezaire

Mary Ann's Legacy

Printed Material:
J. Evetts Haley, "*Charles Goodnight*"
Laura V. Hammer, "*The No-Gun Man of Texas*"
Oral Stories:
Vicki Sybert

Teresita

Printed Material:
Jim O'Neal, "*Ironic Victory*"
Scott Thybony, "*Against All Odds*"
Leon Metz, "*The Buffalo Soldier*"
Robert M. Utley, "*The Indian Frontier of the American West 1846-1890*"
Art T. Barton, "*Black, Buckskin and Blue*"
Caleb Pirtle III & Michael F. Cusak, "*Ft. Clark, the Lonely Sentinel*"
World Wide Web:
Ms. Joni Jordan, "*Black Seminole Indian Scouts*"
Irene Burleson, "*Apache History*"
Martha Meacham, Phd., "*Lipan Apache in Texas*"
Oral Stories:
Katarina Wittich
Directors of Ft. Clark Museum

Conflict in the Frio Canyon

Printed Material:
A. J. Sowell, "*Early Settlers and Indian Fighters of Southwest Texas*"
Alan Stovall, "*Breakes of the Balcones*"
Alan Stovall, "*Upper Nueces Headwater Country*"
George Nelson, "*The Lipan-Apache*"
John Leakey, "*The West That Was*"
Oral Stories:
Miss Sallye Godbold
Lora B. Garrison
George Nelson

To order books, contact:

Linda Kirkpatrick
P.O. Box 128
Leakey, TX 78873

To order by phone call
(830) 232-5308.